Designing Audio Circuits

Designing Audio Circuits

Robert Sontheimer

Elektor Electronics (Publishing)

Elektor Electronics (Publishing)
P.O. Box 1414
Dorchester
England DT2 8YH

The publishers have used their best efforts in ensuring the correctness of the information
 contained in this book. They do not assume, and hereby disclaim, any liability to any party for any
loss or damage caused by errors or omissions in this book, whether such errors or
omissions result from negligence, accident or any other cause.

British Library Cataloguing in Publication Data
A catalogue record for this book is available from the British Library

ISBN 0 905705 50 5

Translation and make-up: A.W. Moore, MSc

First published in the United Kingdom 1998

© Segment BV 1998

Printed in the Netherlands by Giethoorn-NND, Meppel

Contents

Other books from Elektor Electronics

301 Circuits (ISBN 0 905705 12 2)

302 Circuits (ISBN 0 905705 25 4)

303 Circuits (ISBN 0 905705 26 2)

304 Circuits (ISBN 0 905705 34 3)

305 Circuits (ISBN 0 905705 36 X)

306 Circuits (ISBN 0 905705 43 2)

Build your own AF valve amplifiers (ISBN 0 905705 39 4)

Build your own Electronic Test Instruments (ISBN 0 905705 37 8)

Build your own high-end audio equipment (ISBN 0 905705 40 8)

Data Book 3: Peripheral Chips (ISBN 0 905705 30 0)

Data Book 4: Peripheral Chips (ISBN 0 905705 32 7)

Data Sheet Book 2 (ISBN 0 905705 27 0)

Faultfinding in Computers and Digital Circuits (ISBN 0 905705 60 2)

I²C Bus (ISBN 0 905705 47 5)

Lasers: Theory and Practice (0 905705 52 1)

Matchbox: Single Board Computer (0 905705 53 X)

Microprocessor Data Book (ISBN 0 905705 28 9)

PC Service & Repair (ISBN 0 905705 41 6)

PICs in Practice (ISBN 0 905705 51 3)

SCSI: The Ins and Outs (ISBN 0 905705 44 0)

Short Course 8051/8032 Microcontrollers & Assembler (ISBN 0 905705 38 6)

SMT Projects (ISBN 0 905705 35 1)

ST62 Microcontrollers (ISBN 0 905705 42 4)

Teach Yourself Word 97 (0 905705 59 9)

The CD-ROM System (ISBN 0 905705 46 7)

1. Circuit fundamentals

When an audio signal passes through an electronic circuit, undesired byproducts are formed. These usually manifest themselves as noise, hum, crackling or distortions and are often not only audible but also disturbing. Clearly, if a circuit is to be suitable for hi-fi applications, any impairment must be kept to an absolute minimum with the aid of suitable networks and proper design. The designer should always bear in mind that any deviation from the original signal that can be heard is unacceptable.

This applies to almost all audio circuits, with the possible exception of those with very high amplification factors. For instance, some noise is virtually unavoidable when the input signal is very small. This also applies to circuits that contain some sort of delay network.

Before we can consider how noise, hum, and other distortions can be suppressed, it is necessary to understand the exact nature of these phenomena.

Noise

In audio technology, noise is always specified as a signal-to-noise ratio. This refers not only to noise as such, but to any signal voltage at the output that was not present at the input. For instance, hum is included in the ratio, even though it plays only a subordinate role.

The signal-to-noise ratio indicates exactly to what extent the interference voltages are lower than the wanted signal, in other words how much below the signal level the noise level is. The signal-to-noise ratio is normally expressed in decibels, which will be reverted to later.

The nature of noise

Mathematically speaking, noise is a composite of a number of signals at many, varying frequencies. It is a random quantity, which generally has no regular or repetitive character. Although random noise may be used to analyse the behaviour of an audio system, it is usually an unwanted feature. Random noise does not have a specific frequency but covers a wide range of frequencies.

White and pink noise

A distinction must be made between white and pink noise. White noise (lower trace in Figure 1-1) has equal energy throughout the frequency range from zero to infinity. The energy of pink noise (upper trace in Figure 1-1) on the other hand is inversely proportional to frequency in a (limited) frequency spectrum. Both types of noise, although generally regarded as unwanted are often used for test purposes. White noise sounds like the speech sibilant 'ss', while pink noise sounds like the speech consonant 'ff'. The names 'white' and 'pink' derive from the spectral division of visible colours (white light contains all colours, while pink light is filtered). The noise produced by electronic circuits is usually white.

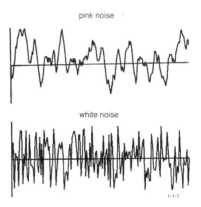

pink noise

white noise

1-1-1

Figure 1-1.
Noise waveforms: pink
(upper trace) and white
(lower trace)

Origin of noise

When a current flows through an conductor, the electron flow is never quite uniform, and this results in irregularities that manifest themselves as noise. These irregularities are particularly noticeable in semiconductors, but also in resistors. It is therefore prudent to use low-noise semiconductors and metal-film resistors in good quality audio circuits. In anticipation of Chapter 6, note that, in order to reduce the noise level, the impedance of semiconductors should be low.

Another source of noise is the magnetic tape used to record audio signals. Some of the tiny magnetic particles contained in the coating of the tape do not align themselves properly during recording and so create random signals, that is, noise. Also, even the best tape does not have a coating of uniform thickness, and this also results in noise.

The noise, heard as hiss, can be largely eliminated by a higher tape speed, a wider soundtrack, or the use of a noise suppression-system, such as Dolby. The basis of such a system is that during the recording the amplitude differences between low and high frequencies is reduced, so that soft passages are recorded at a rather higher level than louder ones. This process is reversed during playback, so that noise is attenuated and the orignal dynamics of the recorded music are retrieved.

Hum

Hum results when the mains frequency gets on to the audio signal. This may be caused by inductive or capacitve coupling, by hum voltage on the earth return, by the series connection of a number of audio units, or by a badly functioning power supply. The latter cause is easily remedied by the use of a suitable voltage regulator, such as a 7815 or 7915.

Hum through inductive coupling

Inductively coupled hum is normallyy caused by the nearness of the mains transformer to signal-carrying conductors or components. Such conductors or components act like windings of the transformer resulting in a voltage being induced in them, which is then added to the signal proper. Much of this effect may be eliminated by placing the relevant conductor or component away from the transformer if at all possible and certainly making sure that it is at right angles to the transformer winding and not in parallel.

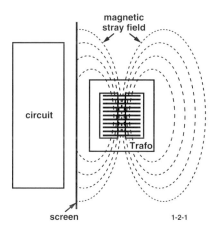

Figure 1-2.
Illustrating the effect of placing a magnetic shield around the transformer.

Figure 1-3.
How hum may be
caused by the series-
connection of a number
of audio units.

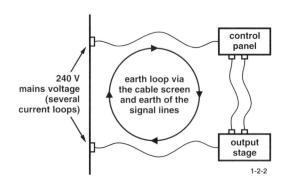

Further improvement may be obtained by the use of a <$itoroidal transformer>, although this is a rather costly remedy. It is better and cheaper to place a mu-metal screen around the transformer, which makes inductive coupling impossible – see Figure 1-2.

Note that such inductive couplings can not only occur within an equipment, but also from one audio unit to another. It is, for instance, not advisable to place a pre-amplifier or effects unit directly on or adjacent to an output amplifier.

Magnetic fields at some distance from an equipment do not normally cause any interference, but they may do on a recording head containing an inductor, which may be found on an electric guitar, for instance. The (intentional) distortion pro-vided by such a guitar is based on high amplification and the resulting clipping of the signal. The tiny voltage produced by any magnetic field, however weak, will also be amplified and cause unwanted interference. The remedy here lies in the use of a dual-coil pick-up: the two coils are connected in series but in anti-phase.

Hum caused by capacitive stray fields

It is well known that an amplifier with open input circuit generates a strong hum when the input terminals are touched. This is caused by a capacitive stray field. The human body and metal parts or current-carrying conductors acts as a capacitve element, or an antenna as it were that picks up all sorts of electric field. If one were to sit in an earthed cage, the effect would not occur. Any electric field is screened and any capacitive action is then to the cage, that is, earth. This is also effected by surrounding signal-carrying conductors with an earthed screen.

Screening inside an equipment may also be needed, say, when small signals are only a few centimetres away from high-impedance parts as is the case, for instance, when signal-carrying conductors are very close to the input terminals. In such cases, it is necessary to screen all signal-carrying conductors or encase the relevant circuit in a mu-metal screen (which must be earthed, of course).

Bear in mind that capacitive interaction may also occur between two or more signal-carrying conductors inside an equipment, which may affect the channel separation, for instance. A particularly critical situation arises when a non-screened input lead runs parallel with a non-screened output lead. The resulting capacitive coupling between the input and output may cause the circuit to oscillate, particularly if the circuit amplification is high. Since the capacitance is very small, the oscillations lie in the very-high or even ultra-high frequency bands (VHF and UHF), which in an audio unit are not readily detected. It is clearly important that in audio circuits signal-carrying leads are not close together other than over very short distances, and even then only if absolutely unavoidable.

Hum caused by different earth potentials

When a single audio unit is powered by several sources, it often happens that a strong hum voltage is generated owing to the difference in potential between the various conductor screens. This may also happen when the mixing panel is situated in a different location and thus uses a different mains outlet. (Translator's note: such a potential difference is highly unlikely in case of a unified earth as in the UK). The screens of the various leads are internally linked to the earth line of the audio signal. Any hum, even at a level of only a few millivolts, is then superimposed via the earth lead on to the music signal. It is normally sufficient to power the various units from the same mains socket to remedy this situation. It is ill-advised to interrupt a screen that is suspected of causing trouble. It may well work satisfactorily, but it is almost certainly at the cost of the reliability of the system.

Harmonic distortion

Harmonic distortion is a phenomenon that is often given an exaggerated importance. Audio enthusiasts proudly point to the data sheets of their installation that show an harmonic distortion of 0.001%. What is the point of this, however, when even the best loudspeaker enclosures have a harmonic distortion of some 2–3 per cent?

What is harmonic distortion?

In general, harmonic distortion is the sum of all non-linear distortion that occurs during the processing of an audio signal. It should be borne in mind that a musical note consists generally of the simultaneous sounding of a group of

Figure 1-4.
The relationship
between a musical note
(upper trace), the fun-
damental tone, and the
first and second over-
tones (also called har-
monics or upper
partials).

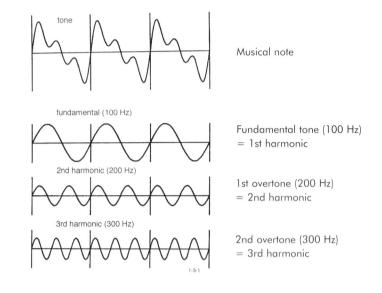

tone

Musical note

fundamental (100 Hz)

Fundamental tone (100 Hz)
= 1st harmonic

2nd harmonic (200 Hz)

1st overtone (200 Hz)
= 2nd harmonic

3rd harmonic (300 Hz)

2nd overtone (300 Hz)
= 3rd harmonic

1-3-1

tones. The frequency of each tone is normally related to the fundamental, that is, the generating, tone by the equation $A=nf$, where n is an integer, f is the fundamental frequency, and A is the frequency of a tone in the series. These relationships are shown in Figure 1-4.

If a simple sine wave is passed through a circuit, such as an amplifier, the waveform of the output is no longer the same as that of the input, that is, some distortion has occurred. The form this distortion may take is shown, in a rather exaggerated way, in Figure 1-5. The distortion caused by a well-designed circuit is nowhere near as serious and certainly not visible on this scale.

Such distortion is the sum of the overtones whose amplitudes are, of course, very small. The distortion factor is the ratio of the generated overtones to the overall signal, that is, the original (input) signal plus all harmonics. If the harmonics constitute one hundredth of the overall signal, the harmonic distortion is 1%. It is clear from this how very small the distortion of the fundamental tone, which determines the pitch of the note, is when the harmonic distortion is, say, 0.01%.

As mentioned, a musical note consists of the fundamental tone and a large number of overtones. Each of these sine waves is affected in the same way as the fundamental. Nevertheless, only a single sinusoidal signal is used to measure the harmonic distortion under defined conditions. Figure 1-5 shows the way different kinds of distortion affect the input signal. It is evidently impossible

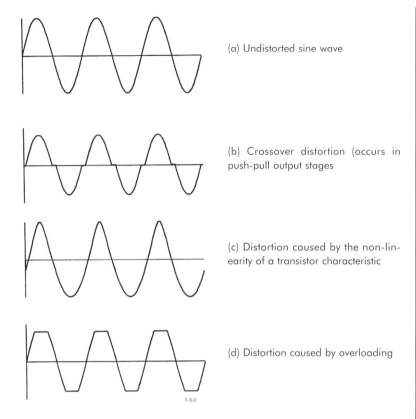

(a) Undistorted sine wave

(b) Crossover distortion (occurs in push-pull output stages

(c) Distortion caused by the non-linearity of a transistor characteristic

(d) Distortion caused by overloading

1-3-2

Figure 1-5.
Undistorted sine wave
(a), and the effects of
different causes of dis-
tortion (b–d)

to say at what level distortion becomes audible. If only the 2nd and 3rd harmonic are generated, the distortion is smaller than when many overtones are produced. It also depends on the type of music when distortion becomes audible or even disturbing.

Causes and remedies of harmonic distortion

All components that have a non-linear characteristic, such as transistors, diodes, integrated circuits, and so on, aid in the production of distortion. Figure 1-6a shows the basic circuit of a push-pull output stage. Since the transistors have insufficient base voltage (<0.7 V), there is no output as long as the level of the input signal is below 0.7 V. In this situation, some crossover distortion as shown in Figure 1-5b occurs. This distortion becomes negligible when an appropriate base voltage is applied as in Figure 1-6b.

A different kind of distortion occurs in a simple amplifier as shown in Figure

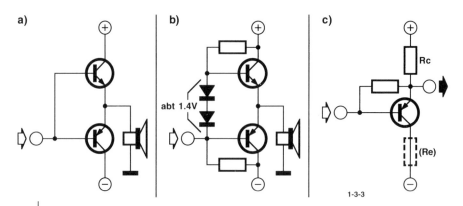

a) b) c)

abt 1.4V

Rc

(Re)

1-3-3

Figure 1-6.
Circuit diagram of
push-pull output stage
with inadequate base
voltage (a) and with
proper base voltage (b).
In (c) is the circuit dia-
gram of a simple volt-
age amplifier.

1-6c. The collector current is linear with respect to the base current, but this is not linear with respect to the base voltage owing to the non-linearity of the diode characteristic. This gives rise to the kind of distortion illustrated in Figure 1-5c. This kind of distortion is virtually eliminated by the use of feedback obtained by, say, a resistor such as R_E. Moreover, because of the additional emitter resistor, the amplification is smaller but better defined: it depends on the ratio R_C to R_E.

Figure 1-7.
With a small input sig-
nal, there is no distor-
tion. When the amplifi-
cation is increased
more and more, the
waveform becomes
increasingly distorted
from trapezoidal to
rectangular.

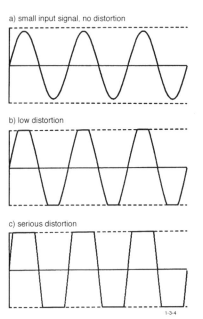

a) small input signal, no distortion

b) low distortion

c) serious distortion

1-3-4

8

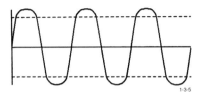

1-3-5

Figure 1-8.
When amplitude clipping is effected by diodes, the waveshape is altered more gently than with supply voltage limiting.

Significance of distortion in practice

In modern circuit technology, distortion is nowhere near the problem it once was. The circuits presented in this book are invariably based on operational amplifiers (op amps), such as the TL074. Because of the enormous amplification these devices have, they can only be used with appropriate feedback and this reduces any distortion greatly.

The distortion in circuits whose amplification is controlled by voltage or current, such dynamic compressors, limiters, noise suppressors, and similar, is rather larger. Such circuits are normally designed on the basis of special integrated circuits – ICs – that have some sort of analogue multiplier. In these circuits, distortion factors of about 0.5% are a commonplace. But even at this level, high by modern standards, the distortion cannot be heard. It can only be discerned when a pure sinousoidal tone is passed through the circuit at the same time as the normal signal

The situation is completely the reverse in the case of distortion generators as used, for instance, in effects units for electric guitars. In these circuits, the signal is amplified to such a degree that clipping of the waveform as shown in Figure 1-5d takes place. If the amplification is raised more, a situation as in Figure 1-7 arises. The original sine wave first becomes trapezoidal and then rectangular.

Amplitude clipping may be obtained in two ways. In one, the supply voltage limits the voltage swing, and in the other diodes are used to limit the signal level, but their effect is not so drastic as shown in Figure 1-8.

Intermodulation distortion

In general, when harmonic distortion is generated, there is also (some) intermodulation distortion. Intermodulation distortion results from spurious combination-frequency components in the output of an amplifier when two or more sinusoidal voltages are applied to the input simultaneously, but it may also result from intermodulation within the waveform, especially when this is complex.

If, for instance, the input signals are at 300 Hz and 400 Hz respectively, the output may include frequencies of 100 Hz and 700 Hz, apart from the original frequencies, of course.

Fortunately, the amplitudes of intermodulation distortion signals are very small since, in contrast to harmonic distortion, frequencies are generated that did not occur in the original signal.

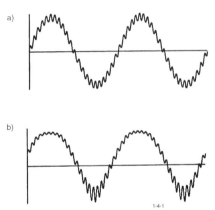

1-4-1

The cause of intermodulation distortion

In general, intermodulation distortion, like harmonic distortion, is caused by components with non-linear characteristic. In Figure 1-9a, a low-level, high-frequency signal is superimposed on a high-level, low-frequency signal. The feeding of this composite signal through a non-linear circuit, whose amplification is higher in the lower range than in the higher, causes each signal to be modulated by the other. The resulting waveform is shown in Figure 1-9b. It is seen that the high-frequency component in the lower range has attained a higher amplitude, depending on the low-frequency response.

The IMD is normally very small and presents no problems. It is modern practice to design for IMD to be below 0.01 per cent over the range 30 Hz to 20 kHz and at all signal levels below the onset of clipping.

Frequency reponse

The frequency response describes the relationship between frequency and amplification in an audio circuit. If a signal is to be processed linearly, the amplification must be the same for all frequencies within the signal. If the tone control of an amplifier is turned, the frequency response is changed. This means that high or low frequencies are amplified to a higher or lesser degree. Such changes in the signal are sometimes called linear distortion. Note, however, that when distortion is mentioned, this almost invariably means non-linear distortion This has nothing to do with the frequency response, although in both cases the signal is distorted.

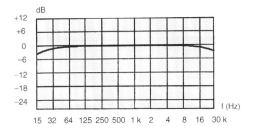

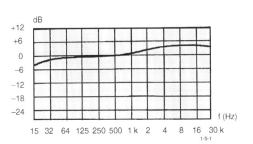

Figure 1-10. Typical frequency response of a good-quality circuit (upper diagram) and of a circuit in which the high frequencies dominate (lower diagram).

The frequency response of a circuit is measured by applying a sine wave to its input that is swept slowly over the frequency range of 20 Hz to 20 kHz. The output measured at various frequencies is then plotted on a diagram as shown in Figure 1-10. If the circuit is of good quality, the response curve may look like that in the upper diagram, from which it is evident that output is fairly constant over the frequency range. The lower diagram shows the response of a circuit in which the higher frequencies are dominant.

Note that the x-axes in the diagrams in Figure 1-10 are drawn on a logarithmic scale, since this gives much clearer picture of the response curve, and is also more representative of human hearing.

Typical frequency responses

If one listens to, say, an audio tape cassette, the frequency responses of the cassette deck, the amplifier, the loudspeakers, and the room all combine. Each of these responses is, of course, typical of the relevant element in the chain, of which the loudspeakers are invariably the weakest link.

Loudspeakers and headphones

Even expensive loudspeakers do not give a flat frequency response over the whole audio range and, moreover, the frequency response is strongly dependent on the acoustics of the listening space and on the angle between the listener and the axes of the loudspeakers. Headphones generally give a better performance, because the sound from them is not affected by reflections from the walls of, and objects in, the listening space.

Cassette decks

Cassette decks have a particular problem as regards the frequency response. Because of the relative low tape speed of 4.75 cm s^{-1}, it is hardly possible to record frequencies above 15 kHz on to the tape. A single oscillation of a signal at this or higher frequency has to be accommodated in a space of only $^{3}/_{1000}$ mm. When it is considered that a single magnetizing element has a finite size, it will be realized that there are real limits here. However, even at lower frequencies the frequency response is not uniform and these deviations are magnified when a noise reduction circuit is used.

Microphones

Depending on their design and construction, different microphones have completely different frequency responses. Dynamic microphones with a good frequency response are very expensive since their relatively large moving mass presents a number of problems to the designer. Electret capacitor microphones with a good frequency response are much cheaper, but this type is prone to be overdriven at high sound pressures.

It should also be borne in mind that the frequency response of a microphone is degraded to some degree by the acoustics of the performing space, particularly when the sound source is some distance away from the micro-phone.

Microphones
The frequency response of most compact disc (CD) players is excellent. However, those with analogue filters at their output may have slight humps in the high frequencies, although these are normally not audible.

Amplifiers
Most amplifiers, particularly those designed for hi-fi applications, generally have an excellent frequency response, except some at the lower end of the price range. The frequency response of instrument amplifiers naturally accords with the application of the instrument.

How important is the frequency response?
As pointed out earlier, the loudspeakers are by far the weakest link in the chain of audio equipment and it could, therefore, be argued that the frequency response of the other units is of no relevance. That is, however, not so. Each further degradation is audible in a direct comparison test, even if it concerns only a few decibels difference. In general, it may be said that a hump in the frequency response is more readily heard than a dip. This is especially so when it concerns a fairly narrow frequency range. Also, fluctuations in the frequency response are more readily heard at high frequencies than at low ones.

Some points to observe in the designing and constructing of audio equipment are as follows.

Normally a complete unit consists of several sub-units, such as a preamplifier, effects circuit, impedance converter, output amplifier. These units are normally capacitively coupled to prevent direct voltages and very-low-frequency signals being transferred from one unit to another. If the value of these capaci-

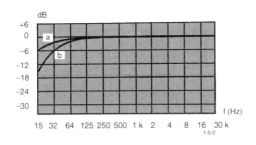

Figure 1-11.
Theoretical and practical cut-off frequency resulting from coupling capacitors.

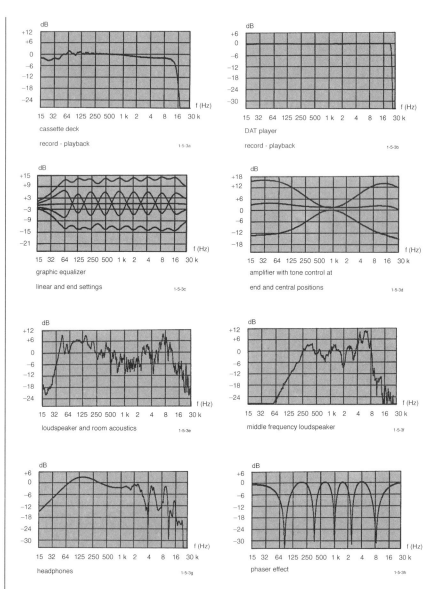

cassette deck

record - playback   1-5-3a

DAT player

record - playback   1-5-3b

graphic equalizer

linear and end settings   1-5-3c

amplifier with tone control at

end and central positions   1-5-3d

loudspeaker and room acoustics   1-5-3e

middle frequency loudspeaker   1-5-3f

headphones   1-5-3g

phaser effect   1-5-3h

tors is chosen to give a lower cut-off frequency of, say, 20 Hz, the practical limit is more likely to be 35 Hz (see Figure 1-11). It is, therefore, advisable to take a value that results in a theoretical cut-off frequency of, say, 5 Hz to obtain a satisfactory practical value.

The upper cut-off frequencxy is determined by the active components, that is, the ICs, transistors, and so on. Operational amplifiers working with high amplification (greater than ×50) may give problems at high frequencies, however. It is advisable if higher amplification is needed to use two or more op amps in cascade (series). An amplification of, say, ×100 is obtained by cascading two op amps each of which has an amplification of ×10. In this way it is possible to ensure that the overall amplification remains constant to well above 20 kHz.

Typical frequency response curves for various audio units are shown in Figure 1-12. Bear in mind that the frequency response of different manufacturers may, of course, deviate from these representations.

Input and output impedance

A complete audio installation consists of several units and subunits each of which has a different input and output impdance. Almost without exception, and it does not matter whether commercial or home-designed units are considered, these units operate in an overmatching arrangement. This means that the output impedance of a unit is normally much smaller than the input impedance of the unit it is connected to.

For instance, if the output of a CD player with an output impedance of 1 kΩ is applied to an amplifier that has an input impedance of 50 kΩ, it is hardly loaded so that a signal at a level of only a few per cent of its true value is fed to the amplifier.

Loudspeakers are also operated in an overmatching configuration, even when the amplifier output is specified as 4 Ω or 8 Ω. This is, of course, not wrongly specified, but the input impedance of the loudspeaker causes the true output impedance to be only a few milliohms.

The often heard opinion that the input and output impedances should be equal if at all possible is erroneous. It is, for instance, perfectly possible to link a low-impedance microphone to a high-impedance amplifier input, provided that this is properly designed. Unfortunately, even expensive equipment from well-known manufacturers often contains a poorly designed preamplifier that has an input with a noise factor fifty times greater than a properly designed circuit would have. This subject will be reverted to in Chapter 6.

Connecting cables

Connecting cables serve to pass the music signal from the pick-up, micro-phone, or similar to the audio circuits and thence to the loudspeakers.

Screening

To prevent ambient interference from affecting the audio signal, the cables car-rying these signals should be contained in an earthed screen. Such a screen is imperative when the signal level is small or when the output impedance of the signal source is high. This means that all cables linking pick-ups, microphones, and similar sources, to amplifiers must be screened. Generally, this is not necessary in case of the link between a CD player or a cassette deck and an amplifier, but it does no harm, of course.

Figure 1-13. Representative dia-grams of single-screened and double-screened cables.

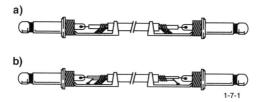

a)

b)

1-7-1

Figure 1-13a shows a representative sketch of a popular single screened audio cable. In this the lead serves as the signal carrier and the screen as the earth return. A rather better cable is shown in 1-13b, which has two leads, of which one is the signal carrier and the other the earth return, while the screen is earthed at one end only (it normally does not matter which end). Any inter-ference picked up by the screen cannot be added to the signal. Nevertheless, the advantage over the single screened cable is very slight and may not justify the extra cost.

Balanced connections

A different, high-quality type of connection is the balanced link shown in Figure 1-14, which is normally used in professional audio installations. In this type of link, the audio signal is sent over two leads in antiphase. The amplifier to which the signals are applied corrects their phase relationship whereupon the two can be added together. Any interference signals induced in the leads are in phase so that the phase inverter in the amplifier causes them to cancel one another. Even so, the cable used is screened. Naturally, this kind of link can be used only if the relevant audio units have balanced inputs and outputs, which is not usual in the case of consumer hi-fi equipment.

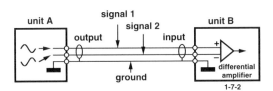

Figure 1-14.
Diagram of a balanced audio link.

Cable quality

In any cable, whether balanced or otherwise, the leads with respect to one another and particularly with respect to the screen form a small capacitance. The value of this capacitance depends on the construction of the cable, for instance, its thickness, and its length (double the length = double the capacitance). The value is normaly in the picofarad range and its effect is not normally discernible unless the signal source has a high-impedance output. In that case, the cable behaves as a low-pass filter with a cut-off frequency of ≤ 20 kHz, so that the high frequencies may be affected adversely. This is a particular problem with inductive pick-ups, such as used with electric guitars, since these are high-impedance at high frequencies, and may therefore even form a resonant circuit with the cable capacitance.

Loudspeaker cable

Loudspeaker cable is a subject in itself. All that has been said so far about screening does not apply to this type of cable. Also, the capacitance of the cable is of no importance. There is, however, a property of loudspeaker cable that is important: its resistance, which depends largely on the cable diameter. Since the nominal input impedance of a loudspeaker is 4 Ω or 8 Ω, the cable resistance must be much smaller to prevent loss of power.

Another factor which is often a topic of conversation is that thin loudspeaker cable adversely affect the quality of the sound. This has a ring of truth to it, but is usually highly exaggerated. Consider that about 7 Ω of an 8 Ω drive unit is formed by the reactance of the copper wire from which the voice coil is wound. Adding about 0.5 Ω cable resistance to this can hardly affect the loudspeaker performance to a great extent. This may, of course, change in the far future when the voice coil is made from superconductive wire.

The cable resistance is readily calculated:

Total resistance (Ω) = 2(length in metres/50×cross-section area in mm^2)

The result must be multiplied by 2 since the cable has two conductors.

Plugs and sockets

There are, of course, numerous types of plugs and sockets used to terminate the cables. It is many designers' practical experience that the most expensive types are certainly not always the best. A good example is the use of plugs and sockets with gold-plated terminals. This is a superfluous luxury. True, their contact resistance is small, but that is in most cases not the problem. However, gold plating looks good.

Figure 1-15.
Various points in a
6.3 mm audio plug that
may cause clicks and
crackles.

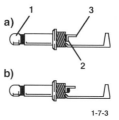

1-7-3

The popular 6.3 mm audio connectors often have a deficiency that has nothing to do with their terminals. This flaw is manifested by clicks and crackles that are seemingly caused by a break in the cable or poor soldering. On close inspection, it appears that the cause is a loose connection in the plug or socket itself (see Figure 1-15). In that case, the signal terminal (1) is easily turned in its enclosure. Contact point (2) is then also turned and has no firm connection with the soldering tab (3). This flaw may be remedied by applying a hot heavy-duty soldering iron to the contact point.

Another cause of bad contact is sometimes found in a board- or chassis-mounted socket. It may happen that the contact spring is slightly bent so that it cannot press firmly enough on the terminal of the mating plug. Here, the remedy is, of course, to bend the spring back slightly to reestablish a good contact.

Valves versus transistors

Many people think that valve amplifiers are, or should be, dead – a relic of a glorious past. This is, however, not the opinion of many musicians, particularly guitarists. They feel strongly that valve amplifiers are considerable superior to solid-state ones, and, in fact, many guitar amplifiers are valve types. But even apart from this, the valve amplifier is making somewhat of a come-back.

Differences

In general, compared with solid-state amplifiers, valve amplifiers operate with much larger signal voltages and smaller signal currents. This means that the circuits used in them have a much higher impedance, which is, of course, a disadvantage as far as the loudspeaker output is concerned. Therefore, valve amplifiers need fairly large (and costly) output transformers, whereas most solid-state circuits can drive a loudspeaker directly.

The power drain of a valve amplifier is higher, which is largely because of the heating of the filament.

A finite time is needed by valve amplifiers before they are operational: this is because the valve heaters take time to reach the appropriate temperature.

A very real difference is the distortion: valve amplifiers are normally more prone to distortion, but this is softer. This means that the level of the lower harmonics is much higher than that of the higher ones.

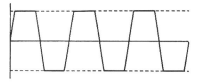

overloaded transistor amplifier (top) and

overloaded valve amplifier (bottom)

Figure 1-16.
Distortion in an over-driven solid-state output amplifier (top) and in a valve output amplifier (bottom).

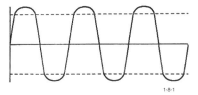

1-8-1

The difference in distortion between an overdriven valve output amplifier and a solid-state one is shown in Figure 1-16. This illustration shows why many guitarists prefer a valve amplifier over a solid-state one. It should be noted, however, that the soft distortion of a valve amplifier can be achieved in a solid-state amplifier with the aid of transistors or integrated circuits. Germanium diodes may also prove very useful.

Whatever opnion one may have, in the end, judging the quality of music and that of an audio installation is a subjective test: it is the pleasure obtain-ined from listening to music that counts.

Acoustic placebo effect

The placebo effect in medicine is well known; that in acoustics not so well. In this section, the effect related to audio and hi-fi listeners will be considered. It concerns some comparisons between output amplifiers, a cassette recording and the original sound, and digital recordings.

Output amplifiers

In an evaluation of two audio output amplifiers, listeners were asked whether they could hear a discernible difference in the sound produced by the two. The audio amplifiers were an expensive one (with gold-plated connectors) costing around £1500 and a much less expensive one of about £225. The same loud-speakers and loudspeaker cable were used with both amplifiers. The listeners could not see which of the amplifiers was used to drive the loudspeakers. The amplifiers were set to the same sound level and switched by means of a special change-over selector. No one could hear any difference even after the ampli-fiers had been switched over a dozen times.

Cassette recording and original sound

A copy made on a cassette recorder is normally not of the same quality as the original. The main reasons for this are the distortion, the frequency response, and the signal-to-noise ratio. Although the signal-to-noise ratio may be im-proved with Dolby-C, this will degrade the frequency response slightly more.

For the evaluation, a fairly inexpesive cassette deck was used, whose fre-quency response was measured with Dolby-C on, whereupon any fluctuations in the response were removed by means of a special filter. A recording was then made of a compact disc.

When the original CD and the cassette were played back, again via a special change-over selector, so that listeners could not know which of the two they were listening to, several stated that they could not hear a difference. Some others said that they could hear a slight difference and thought that the CD was better, but there were also some who could hear a slight difference but thought the cassette better! This is an absolutely astonishing result when it is borne in mind that a cassette recording at full drive produces a total distortion of a few per cent. Who said that most of us can hear a distortion of 0.1 per cent?

Digital recordings

Although compacts discs have long taken over from vinyl records, there are still people who are not convinced ot the sound quality of these discs. Many people who grew up with vinyl records find that CDs sound rather high-pitched.

In the present evaluation, a copy was made on a good-quality DAT recorder• of a CD, whereupon the recording and CD were played back as in the previous evaluation by random switching between them via a special selector. This evaluation also showed that listeners could not detect an audible difference between the cassette recording (played back in the standard mode) and the original CD. Only when the DAT recorder was switched to long play did listeners hear a difference. This is because a DAT recorder in the long-play mode uses a sampling rate of only 30 kHz, which makes the frequency response cut off at about 15 kHz.

It appears from listeners' comments that digital recordings are considered to sound rather more high-pitched than the original music. Nevertheless, it is admitted that the reasons for this sentiment may be found elsewhere. The compact disc is the first sound carrier that makes possible a true linear reproduction of all audible frequencies, and this may at times sound rather unusual. In this context, it should be borne in mind that even VHF FM stations do not transmit frequencies above 15 kHz. Cassette recorders, too, limit high frequencies in a similar manner. The frequency range of record players depend on the speed at which the stylus runs in the groove of the record. When the record is being played, the radius of this gets smaller and smaller the more the stylus moves towards the centre. Near the centre of the record, the speed of the stylus no longer suffices to reproduce the whole audio range. There may be an-

* Owing to poor sales, the DAT recorder is no longer in production. [Transl.]

other reason that CDs sound unusual. Older recordings that have been on the market for years on vinyl discs, have been rerecorded on CDs with modern studio techniques, whereby their frequency spectrum has been enlarged.

2. Components

In this chapter, all components used in the audio circuits in this book will be discussed. Particular attention will be paid to quality and tolerances, and also where savings can be made without sacrificing quality.

Resistors

Resistors are the most commonly used components and, fortunately, also the cheapest. Resistors for use in audio circuits should generally have a small tolerance since they determine the amplification and, in filters, together with capacitors, determine the cut-off or resonant frequency.

The use of metal film resistors is strongly recommended since they generate far less noise than carbon types, and that is, of course, very important in audio applications. Most metal film resistors are available with small tolerances.

It is, of course, possible in most circuits to see which resistors should be close-tolerance types and which not. However, because of the small cost of resistors, such selection is hardly worthwhile. For all circuits in this book, it is invariably recommended to use metal film resistors with 1% tolerance.

Power rating

In many cases, ¼ watt power rating of resistors is perfectly adequate. Where it is not, this is specified in the parts lists accompanying the various circuits in this book. In case of higher power rating, as required in some circuits, carbon or wirewound resistors with a tolerance of 5 per cent may be used.

The colour code of resistors is given in Chapter 3.

Capacitors

Capacitors are used for three main purposes:
- blocking direct voltages;
- determining frequency;
- smoothing of rectified voltages.

Owing to these diverse requirements, there is a wide variety of types of capacitor. For instance, to block direct voltages, capacitors need not be close-tolerance types. Coupling capacitors form in conjunction with the input of the stage they are connected to a high-pass filter whose cut-off frequency is of the order of 5 or 10 Hz. Normally, coupling capacitors are film types rated at 40 V or 63 V, which is more than adequate when the power lines are ±15 V.

The rating of frequency-determining capacitors also need not be higher than 40 V. However, their tolerance must be appreciably better and should be ≤ 5%. In many cases, such as for instance narrow-band equalizer circuits, even that is not good enough and 2½% is specified, even though this makes the circuit a little more expensive.

Figure 2-1.
Smoothing of a
pulsating direct voltage
(rectified alternating
voltage).

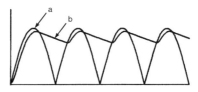

a) pulsating direct voltage

b) with load and smoothing capacitor   2-2-1

Smoothing capacitors are usually electrolytic types normally only found in power supplies. They have as task the flattening of the rectified half-wave pulses as shown in Figure 2-1. The larger the value of the capacitor, the smaller the voltage dips between successive half-waves. Close tolerances are not required: electrolytic capacitors with a tolerance of +100% and −20% are quite common in power supply circuits. The maximum voltage rating of these capacitors is important, however. For instance, in the case of a 15 V power supply, the electrolytic capacitors should be rated at not less than 35 V.

Potentiometers
Potentiometers, plugs, sockets, and switches are the only components with movable mechanical parts. They are consequently vulnerable to degradation owing to dust, dirt or rust. The click, scratches, crackles and so on cause by these have made many an audio enthusiast feel like tearing out his/her hair.

The quality of potentiometers should always be first class, but beware: the most expensive ones are not always the best and the least expensive not always the worst. There are now on the market potentiometers completely enclosed in a sealed case of synthetic material, whose wiper is consequently protected against dirt and corrosion. However, if such a potentiometer gives problems like crackling there is not much that can be done, since putting in a drop of sewing machine oil, which often cured the problem in older types, is no longer possible.

The resistance of a potentiometer is, of course, also of importance, although the nominal value may vary quite a bit. For instance, in some circuits a 50 kΩ potentiometer is specified and this may easily be replaced by a 47 kΩ type.

Very important, but so often ignored, is the difference between linear and logarithmic tracks. In linear potentiometers, the track resistance is directly proportional to the angle of rotation, whereas in logarithmic types the track resistance is proportional to the logarithm of the angle of rotation. Which of the two types is needed in a specific case is indicated in the relevant parts list.

Operational amplifiers

Operational amplifiers, op amps, have become an indispensable component in modern circuit technology. In almost any position where earlier transistors were used in an amplifier circuit there are now op amps. An op amp is in essence a complex integrated circuit consisting of transistors and resistors. Because of its unform and clearly definable mode of operation it makes circuit design much easier and, it must be said, normally cheaper.

Terminals of an op amp

The circuit symbol of an op amp is shown in Figure 2-2. The two vertical lines, marked $+U_B$ and $-U_B$ are the terminals for the symmetrical supply voltage. These terminals are not always shown in circuit diagrams, since they are con-

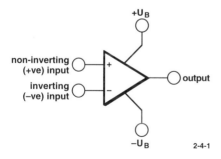

Figure 2-2.
The various terminals of an operational amplifier.

sidered superfluous: everybody knows that a symmetrical power line is needed.

The terminals at the left in Figure 2-2 are the inputs and that at the right is the output. The inputs are termed positive or non-inverting and negative or inverting.

Note that there are op amps that have terminals for frequency compensation or offset compensation, but these are not of interest here.

Operation of an op amp

In theory, all an op amp does is comparing its two inputs. If the potential at the non-inverting input is only slight higher than that at the negative input, the output voltage changes to a level slightly below the positive supply voltage. If, however, the potential at the inverting input is higher than that at the positive input, the output becomes slightly less than the negative supply voltage.

*Figure 2-3.
Mechanical representa-
tion of an operational
amplifier.*

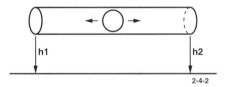

The operation may become clearer with reference to Figure 2-3. This represents a horizontal valve containing a ball. Heights h_1 and h_2 represent the two input voltages, while the position of the ball represents the output potential. As soon as one of the ends is only slightly higher than the other, the ball will roll towards that end.

It may be asked how a component that apparently has only two output states can process and amplify analogue music signals. This is achieved by applying feedback; how this is done is shown in Figure 2-4. For simplicity's sake, the power lines have been omitted.

Assume that the potential at the non-inverting input is slightly higher, say, by

*Figure 2-4.
How feedback is
applied to an oper-
ational amplifier.*

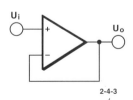

10 mV, than that at the negative input. The output voltage will then tend to rise to U_B. But, owing to the feedback link, this also increases the potential at the negative input. But when this happens, the output will tend to become $-U_B$. An so on. In reality, the output will assume a voltage whereby the two inputs are in balance. This means that the output voltage, U_O, is equal to the input voltage, U_I. The time taken for this equilibrium to be reached is very short indeed: it certainly is not noticeable. This is how a music signal applied to the positive input is faithfully reproduced at the output.

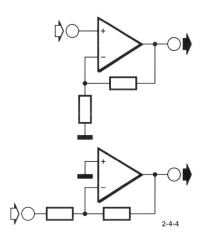

Figure 2-5.
Gain is obtained by
taking the feedback
from a potential divider.

Amplification

Because of the feedback, an op amp becomes a useful component, but it provides as yet no gain since the output signal is equal to the input signal. Amplification will be provided if only part of the output voltage is fed back and this is achieved with the aid of a potential divider as shown in Figure 2-5. The actual operation and calculation of the divider will be discussed in Chapter 4.

An op amp is not perfect

In the considerations thus far it has been assumed that the amplification of an op amp is infinitely high, that is, that the device reacts by a huge change in output for the tiniest change in input. It has also been assumed that the op amp operating with feedback adjusts the difference between the two input voltage to exactly zero. And finally, it has been assumed that the input voltages are not affected, that is, loaded, by the inputs, or, in other words, that the input impedance of an op amp is infinitely high.

These assumptions are not entirely correct: any op amp deviates from this ideal state to some extent. For instance, the gain of an op amp without feedback is not infinite, but anything from ×50,000 to ×100,000. Also, an op amp operating with feedback does not adjust the difference between its inputs to exactly zero but to a few millivolts (offset). And finally, the input impedance of an op amp is not infinitely high, but a few mega-ohms or giga-ohms. All these limitations are, however, hardly noticeable in practice.

Symmetrical power supply

Another amplifier circuit using an op amp is shown in Figure 2-6. In a, this amplifier is powered by a symmetrical ±15 V line. The reason for a ±15 V line is that this enables the central (0 V) potential to be the earth so that the amplifier can swing in either the positive or negative direction. Should a symmetrical supply not be used as in b, the central potential has to be arranged with the aid of a potential divider and regulated by capacitor C_3. Since this potential is not

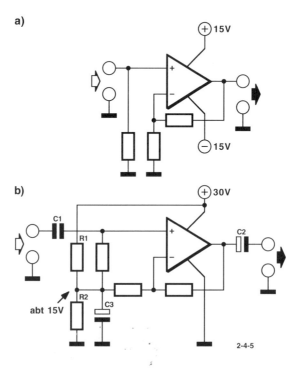

Figure 2-6.
Op amp fed by a symmetrical supply (left) and one supplied by a single power line (right).

28

earth, which is linked to the negative input terminal, capacitors C_1 and C_2 are needed to decouple the supply line.

TL0XX family

The Type TL074 IC is often found in amplifiers, equalizers, and effects units. This is a 14-pin quadruple operational amplifier which is especially suitable for processing music signals. It has some excellent properties:
- low distortion;
- low noise;
- high-impedance JFET (junction field-effect transistor) inputs (10^{12} Ω);
- short-circuit-proof, bipolar output stage.

Another benefit this IC has is that, owing to its popularity, it is readily available and is hardly dearer than a single operational amplifier. Also, since many circuits require at least four op amps (often more), the TL074 will be found in many circuits in this book.

The TL074 is one of a family of several members who are differentiated from one another by the last two digits in their type coding. The first of these digits indicates the type of op amp and the last shows how many op amps there are in the IC. The digits of the various members are shown in the table below.

TL	0	X	X	
			1	single op amp
			2	dual op amp
			4	quadruple op amp
		6		low power version (battery operation)
		7		low-noise version (hi-fi applications)
		8		standard version

The table shows that there are a number of different versions of the IC. Type TL062, for instance, is a dual op amp, low-power version specially intended for circuits in which low current drain is important (battery operation). There are others not shown in the table, which are not of interest in this book.

Figure 2-7.
Pinouts of various
members of the TL0XX
family.

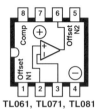
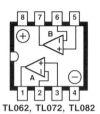

TL061, TL071, TL081   **TL062, TL072, TL082**

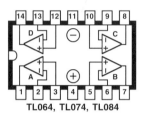

TL064, TL074, TL084   2-5-1

viewed
from above

The pinouts of the single op amps are shown in Figure 2-7. These show that single op amps Type TYL061, TL071, and TL081, have three additional terminals, designated comp and offset (2). These are not used in any circuits in this book. This means that if any of these types of IC is used, the additional terminals are left unconnected.

Technical specifications

Although the TL0xx family has a number of members, their technical specifications are very similar. For instance, a TL071 is identical to both the op amps contained in a TL072, and also with all four contained in the TL074. Even the TL08x versions differ from the others only in a slightly higher noise factor. Thus, the following specifications apply equally to all ICs from the TL071 to the TL084; only those of the low-power versions, TL061 to TL064 are different in some respects.

Limiting values

Maximum supply voltage	36 V or ±18 V
Maximum input voltage	±15 V
Short-circuits at output	Unlimited (fully proof)
Maximum dissipation at 25 °C	680 mW
Maximum storage temperature	−65 °C to +150 °C
Operating temperature	0 °C to +70 °C

Characteristics

(U$_B$ = ±15 V and ambient temperature = 25 °C)

Quantity	Min	Typ	Max	Unit
Input offset voltage		5	15	mV
Offset temperature drift		10		μV/°C
Quiescent input current		30	400	pA
Offset input current		5	200	pA
Common-mode input				
voltage range	±10	±12		V
Output voltage swing				
R$_L$ = 10 kΩ	±12	±13.5		V
R$_L$ = 2 kΩ	±10	±12		V
Voltage amplification	25×10^3	15×10^4		
Bandwidth		3		MHz
Input impedance		10^{12}		Ω
Common-mode suppression	70			dB
Supply voltage suppression	70			dB
Current drain (each op amp)		1.4	2.8	mA

Since not all readers may be acquainted with these terms, here is a further explanation.

Limiting values.
These values are those that the IC can handle. Larger values may destroy the device.

Input offset voltage.
This is the difference between the two input voltages remaining in spite of the feedback.

Offset temperature drift.
This indicates to what extent the offset voltage depends on the ambient temperature.

Quiescent input current.
This is the current with which the inputs load the circuit.

Input offset current.
The difference between the input currents when feedback is applied.

Common-mode input voltage range.
This gives the level of input voltage that does not overload the inputs when the op amp is used as an impedance converter. When the amplification >1, the output is the first to be overloaded.

Output voltage swing.
This is the maximum swing of the output voltage for a given load at the output. In normal operation, it is slightly smaller than the maximum supply voltage.

Voltage amplification.
The amount of amplification in the absence of feedback.

Bandwidth.
Indicates the frequencies at which the voltage amplification drops to unity.

Input resistance.
The value of resistance with which the inputs load the circuit.

Common-mode suppression.
The amount by which in-phase changes in the two input voltages are suppressed in the output signal.

Supply line suppression.
The amount by which interference, hum, and noise, on the power lines are suppressed (70 dB is a factor of about 3000).

Current drain per op amp.
The quiescent current drawn by each op amp in the absence of an input signal and open-circuit output.

3. Important standards

Like all disciplines and technologies, electronics and audio engineering have a number of general standards and agreements: from the plug on headphones to the colour code of resistors. These standards and agreements take on their true importance when one tries to imagine what designing and constructing would be like without them. Imagine what chaos there would be if every producer of equipment had his own standards: it might then be impossible to use, say, a CD player with most amplifiers on the market. And what would have happened if every record producer had used his own standards for the production of CDs?

Most special standards are of no importance to readers of this book, in which only the more important and fundamental standards will be discussed.

Decibel

Basic unit: the Bel – symbol B

The Bel (B) is a basic logarithmic unit (named after Alexander Graham Bell) to express the ratio of two powers, voltages, currents or sound intensities. If, for instance, two power values, P_1 and P_2, differ by n bels, then

$$n = \log_{10}(P_2/P_1).$$

So, 1 B indicates a power gain of 10^1; 2 B one of 10^2; and 5 B.one of 10^5.

When dealing with signal levels, this equation does not hold, since a tenfold increase in voltage means a hundredfold increase in power ($P = U^2/R$ – see Figure 3-1). The equation for voltage ratios differing by n bels becomes

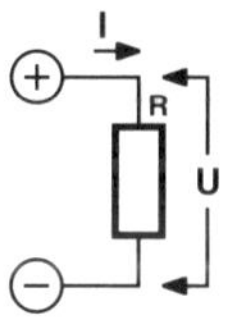

3-1-1

Figure 3-1.
When the voltage, U, is doubled, the current, I, is doubled also and the dissipation, P, across R increases by a factor 4
(2^2).

$$n = 2\log_{10}(U_1/U_2).$$

From Bel to decibel

Normally, signals levels are compared that are close in value, in which case expressing their ratio in bels would result in a very small figure. Since this is inconvenient, the decibel, that is, one tenth of a bel (dB) is normally used in practice. The equations for expressing power ratios and voltage ratios in decibels become:

$$n = 10\log_{10}(P_1/P_2)$$

and

$$n = 20\log_{10}(U_1/U_2).$$

Attenuation

Attenuation, α, is merely an amplification, A, at a factor smaller than 1. The two quantities are equal but have a different sign, that is

$$\alpha = -A \qquad and \qquad \alpha = 20\log_{10}(U_2/U_1)\ \ dB.$$

In other words, if the amplification is 0.5, $A = -6$ dB or $\alpha = 6$ dB.

Advantages of the decibel notation

It may be asked why it is necessary or useful to express amplification in decibels rather than just as a figure. Indeed, amplification is normally stated to be, say, ×14, whereas gain is usually expressed in dB (an amplification of ×14 is the same as a gain of 5 dB). However, the decibel notation has several advantages.

* In the case of a multistage amplifier, the amplications of the various stages need not be multiplied, but, expressed in dB, they are merely added together.
* Quantities expressed in decibels are more convenient to handle, particularly when high amplification is involved. 80 dB is more easily remmebered and handled than an amplification of 10 000.
* Most graphical representations, such as frequency response, are far more easily interpreted on a decibel scale (since the values are in dB, a linear scale may be used – see Figure 3-2.

The table on the next page gives the values in dB for a number of voltage and power

	Amplification		Attenuation	
dB	U_1/U_2	P_1/P_2	U_2/U_1	P_2/P_1
0	1	1	1	1
1	1.12	1.26	0.89	0.79
2	1.26	1.6	0.79	0.63
3	1.4	2	0.71	0.5
4	1.6	2.5	0.63	0.4
5	1.8	3.2	0.56	0.32
6	2	4	0.5	0.25
7	2.2	5	0.45	0.2
8	2.5	6.3	0.4	0.16
9	2.8	7.9	0.35	0.13
10	3.2	10	0.32	0.1
11	3.5	12.6	0.28	0.079
12	4	16	0.25	0.063
13	4.5	20	0.22	0.05
14	5	25	0.2	0.04
15	5.6	32	0.18	0.032
16	6.3	40	0.16	0.025
17	7.1	50	0.14	0.02
18	7.9	63	0.126	0.016
19	8.9	79	0.112	0.013
20	10	10^2	0.1	10^{-2}
30	31.6	10^3	0.032	10^{-3}
40	10^2	10^4	10^{-2}	10^{-4}
50	316	10^5	0.032	10^{-5}
60	10^3	10^6	10^{-3}	10^{-6}
80	10^4	10^8	10^{-4}	10^{-8}
100	10^5	10^{10}	10^{-5}	10^{-10}
120	10^6	10^{12}	10^{-6}	10^{-12}
140	10^7	10^{14}	10^{-7}	10^{-14}

Table 3.1
Conversion of decibels to amplification or attenuation.

Figure 3-2.
Frequency response
curves on a logarithmic
scale and on a linear
scale

a)

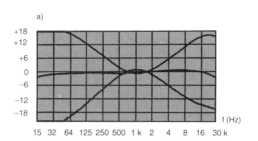

b)

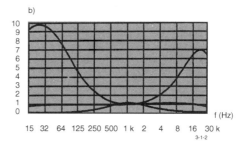

3-1-2

gains and voltage and power losses. Intermediate values are easily assessed. If, for instance, it is desired to know the voltage amplificatrion equivalent to a gain of 46 dB, proceed as follows

20 dB + 20 dB + 6 dB = 46 dB,

and this is equivalent to amplification factors

10×10×2 = 200.

Thus, a gain of 46 dB equals an amplification of ×200.

In this manner, most common and intermediate values can be determined. Some useful, frequently encountered values are

3 dB = voltage amplification of ×1.4 ($\sqrt{2}$)
6 dB = *voltage amplification of ×2*
10 dB = voltage amplification of ×3.2 ($\sqrt{10}$)
20 db = voltage amplification of ×10

Input and output levels

The usual audio output of CD players, cassette recorders, and tuners, is between 400 mV and 600 mV. The output impedance varies from 400 Ω to 3 kΩ. The corresponding input of audio amplifiers is in accord with these values; the input impedance is normally of the order of 20 kΩ to 100 kΩ, which is a great deal higher than the output impedances they are linked to. Because of the uniformity of the output levels, the amplifier inputs 'CD', 'Tape', 'Tuner', and 'Aux' are interchangeable at will. For instance, an additional cassette recorder may be linked to the tuner input or a second CD player to the Aux input without any problems. In the same way, the record input of a cassette deck may be linked to any of the other audio units mentioned earlier. A signal level that is too high or too low can be corrected manually with the recording level control.

A wrong signal level at the input of an amplifier can be corrected, of course, with the volume control. There is a problem, however, when the signal level is too low to provide full drive to the output stages, in which case even with the volume control fully open these stages deliver only part of the full power output. If the signal is too high, on the other hand, the preamplifier or tone control circuit may be overloaded, which causes distortion.

Problems also arise when the various signal sources provide different output levels. This results in the volume control having to be altered every time there is a change-over to a different signal source. In a well-designed audio installation there is no need to adjust the volume control when there is a change-over from, say, the tuner to the CD player or cassette deck.

Nowadays, such problems arise but seldom and then normally with audio units that use 5-pin diode connectors and whose output signal level is rather lower than that of modern units. In such an eventuality, the level matching circuit described in Chapter 6 may offer a remedy.

Phono input and output

As far as their output level is concerned, record players form an exception to the statements in the previous paragraph. This is becaue their signal comes directly from the pick-up, that is, without any electronic preparation as happens in CD players and cassette decks. This means that the signal level and output impedance are determined solely by the properties of the pick-up. In the case of a magnetic pick-up, the signal level is of the order of a few millivolts and the output impedance is frequency-dependent. This means that a suitable preamplifier, such as described in Chapter 6, is required.

A crystal pick-up provides an output of 100 mV to 1 V and therefore does not need a preamplifier. However, its sound quality is not as good as that of a magnetic pick-up, which is therefore far more popular.

Loudspeaker outputs

In the case of loudspeaker outputs, there is, of course, no question of standardized signal levels, since these depend on the amplifier rating and the volume control setting. In the case of high-power amplifiers, the input to the loudspeakers may be anywhere between 100 mV and 50 V (for an output of a few hundred watts).

The impedance at the loudspeaker output terminals of power amplifiers is nowadays normally 4 Ω or 8 Ω. The actual output impedance is much lower, however, since loudspeakers are also operated in an overmatching arrangement. If, for instance, a 2 Ω loudspeaker is connected to such an amplifier, theory predicts a higher output power, but in practice the amplifier will start giving smoke signals after only a few minutes.

RIAA or EIA characteristic

When a long-playing record is played back via a magnetic pickup, the output signal is not proportional to the amplitude of the stylus but to its speed. This means that high frequencies provide a much higher signal than low frequencies. This is because, even with uniform amplitude, the speed of change between positive and negative half-waves is much greater at high frequencies. If the output signal is used directly, the high frequencies on the record should have only a small amplitude, whereupon they would be drowned in the background noise. The low frequencies on the other hand would need such a large amplitude that the distance between the grooves would have to be larger. This in turn would make the playback time of a record pretty short.

These shortcomings have for many years been overcome by the use of a special filter that modifies the frequency response to such an extent that all frequencies can be accommodated on the record with similar amplitude. The preamplifier processes the signal from the pick-up and, with the aid of an *RC* filter, gives it a frequency response as shown in Figure 3-3a, which is the so-called RIAA (Recording Industry Association of America) or EIA (Electronic Industries Association) characteristic. The curve takes advantage of the sensitivity of the human ear at various frequencies to reduce the level of audible noise. It is built up from the response curves of various signel filters with cut-off frequencies of 50 Hz, 500 Hz, and 2120 Hz. The composite of these curves is shown in Figure 3-3b. In a practical curve, the sharp corners are, of course, rounded off as in Figure 3.3a.

Plugs and sockets

The plugs and sockets used to interconnect a variety of consumer audio equipment are subject to standards which are adhered to by virtually all manufacturers world-wide. This means that, in general, equipment from several different manufactuers can be interlinked without any problems and without the need of any special adap-tors.

   Phono plugs and sockets have in the main supplanted the 5-pin DIN types that were used years ago. Loudspeakers generally use spring-loaded clamp connectors that accept the bare wire without the need of a plug. The usual loudspeaker plug of yesteryear has all but disappeared. In music equipment the 6.3 mm jack con-nector is predominant, as is the 3-pin XLR plug and socket for balanced connec-tions.

Resistor colour code

All but high-power resistors carry a colour code that shows the resistance value and tolerance in the shape of bands. The small size of most resistors makes it impossi-ble to print these quantities on the body of these components. Generally, there are four bands (see Figure 3-4), but there are some resistors with five. In these, the first three bands, rather than the first two, give the value (which is then, of course, a little more accurate).

   A few examples to show how the colour code is to be used. Note that values are always in ohms.

Colour code:	brown	black	orange	gold
	1	0	10^3	5% (tolerance).

Colour code:	brown	black	black	red	brown
	1	0	0	10^2	1% (tolerance)

Both examples refer to a 10 000 Ω (10 kΩ) resistor. Since, however, the number of bands and the tolerance are different, only the first two bands are identical. Another example:

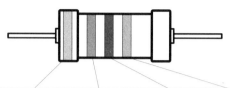

color	1st digit	2nd digit	mult. factor	tolerance
black	–	0	–	–
brown	1	1	$\times 10^1$	±1%
red	2	2	$\times 10^2$	±2%
orange	3	3	$\times 10^3$	–
yellow	4	4	$\times 10^4$	–
green	5	5	$\times 10^5$	±0,5%
blue	6	6	$\times 10^6$	–
violet	7	7	–	–
grey	8	8	–	–
white	9	9	–	–1
gold	–	–	$\times 10^{-1}$	±5%
silver	–	–	$\times 10^{-2}$	±10%
none	–	–	–	±20%

Colour code: yellow   violet   gold   gold

              4   7 10^{-1} 5% (tolerance).

It may, of course, not always be immediately clear in which direction the colour code should be read, but in almost all cases reading in a wrong direction would give an odd result. Also, a colour code cannot start with gold, and the tolerance band is generally slightly further away from the other bands.

Preferred values of resistors

Resistors are commonly sold in six values plus decades. This is know as the E6 series. This can be expanded to 12 values to become the E12 series or to 24 to become the E24 series. The numbers indicate the powers of 10 by which the resistor values increase, that is, $10^{1/6}$, $10^{1/12}$, $10^{1/24}$. Resistors in the E6 series generally have a tolerance of ±20%, those in the E12 series, ±10%, and those in the E24 series, ±5%. However, close-tolerance types are available in all series. The preferred values in the E6 and E12 series are used not only for resistors, but also for capacitors, while those in the E12 series also apply to the rating of zener diodes.

E6 series: 1.0   1.5   2.2   3.3   4.7   6.8

E12 series: as E6 plus
    1.0   1.2   1.5   1.8   2.2   2.7   3.3   3.9   4.7   5.6   6.8   8.2

E24 series: as E12 plus
    1.1   1.2   1.6   2.0   2.4   3.0   3.6   4.3   5.1   6.2   7.5   9.1.

There are more preferred-value series: E48 and E96 with even more precise values. These are normally used in highly accurate potential dividers or in special equipment, audio as well as r.f. The most popular is, however, the E12 series. The circuits in this book invariably use E12 resistors.

In the United Kingdom, resistors are often sold by the BS1852 method of marking. The multiplier is represented by a single letter. For example:

    R = ×1   K = ×1000   M = ×1 000 000
    470R   820K   3M3
    6R8   2K7   10M

To this is added a letter giving the tolerance:
    F = 1%   G = 2%   J = 5%   K = 10%   M = 20%

Capacitor identification (marking)

The marking of capacitors can be confusing, since, for instance, the tolerance is seldom given as a figure but rather by a letter. The value of the capacitance is also normally given by special symbols.

On most capacitors, the value is usually stated as a figure without the relevant unit. In such cases, the unit is either picofarad (pF) or microfarad (μF). If the value is given in nanofarad (nF), at least the 'n' is added to the figure. The zero before the decimal point is normally omitted, so, a value stated as .15 is really 0.15. The decimal point can easily be overlooked!

More and more often, the value of the capacitance is given as a three-digit figure without the relevant unit; the last of the three digits is never a zero. So, 682 might mean a value of 682 pF. This would, however, be a rather odd value. Actually, in this case, the digit 2 indicates two zeros, so that the value in reality is 6800 pF. In the same way, 224 indicates a value of 220000 pF or 0.22 μF.

Tolerance markings

As mentioned earlier, the tolerance of a capacitor is not normally given as a figure but by a letter, usually K or J. Other letters are used, however, as shown in the following table. The letters most often used are indicated by an asterisk.

B	±0.1 pF	K*	±10%	S*	+50%, −20%
C	±0.25 pF	L	±15%	T	+50%, −10%
D	±0.5 pF	M*	±20%	U	+80%, −0%
F	+1 pf	N	±30%	W	+20%, −0%
G	±2 pf	P	+100%, −0%	Y	+50%, −0%
H*	±2.5%	Q	+30%, −10%	Z	+100%, −20%
J*	±5%	R	+30%, −20%		

Some more examples for further clarification:

22nK	0.022 μF, ±10%
473J	0.047 μF, ±5%
10K	10 pF, ±10%
	(or 10 μF if the capacitor is large)
.47S	0.47 μF, +50%, −20%
.01H	0.01 μF, ±2.5%
.1M	0.1 μF, ±20%
4n7J	0.0047 μF, ±5%

4. Basic circuits with op amps

Circuit diagrams of modern effects units, amplifiers, mixing panels, and so on, show certain conspicuous aspects. The first of these is that in today's audio circuit technology virtually all circuits use operational amplifiers. The second is that many circuits as a whole consist of a string of cascaded operational amplifier stages.

It is also noteworthy that such op amp stages are often similar or even identical in whatever equipment they are used. The reason for this is that for each and every function in audio circuits there is a relevant basic circuit. The only differences in actual circuits is the values or ratings or both of the components used. The basic circuits discussed in this chapter will therefore be found back in the circuits in later chapters.

Impedance inverter

The circuit of an impedance converter has already been discussed briefly in the section on 'Operational amplifiers' in Chapter 2. It is perhaps the simplest of all the basic circuits, because other than the op amp no components are needed. The input signal, U_I, is applied directly to the non-inverting (+) input of the op amp (see Figure 4-1). The output signal, U_O, is fed back to the inverting (−) input and is, therefore, identical to U_E, since an op amp with feedback tends to nullify the difference between its two input signals .

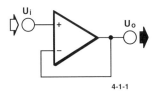

It may be asked what the purpose of such a circuit is if the input and output are identical. It is simply that the input and output resistance are quite different since the input signal is hardly loaded by the non-inverting input: in other words the input resistance is very high.

As far as the output resistance is concerned, assume that $U_\text{I} = 1$ V, so that U_O, and thus the voltage at the inverting input, is also 1 V. The difference between the two input signals is then 0. If now the output is loaded so that U_O drops to, say, 0.8 V, the two input voltages are no longer equal: that at the non-inverting input is 0.2 V higher. This is the case, however, for a fleeting instant, because the op amp rapidly adjusts its output back to 1 V so that the difference at the inputs is zero again. This adjustment happens so fast that it cannot be detected in practice.

This means that the output resistance is load-independent, that is, it is 0 Ω. This is true of all op amp circuits, amplifiers, filters and others, with feedback. There is, of course, a limit because the output current of an op amp is at most a few milli-amperes. So, if for instance a loudspeaker were driven directly by an op amp, the circuit would be overloaded when the power nears about 100 mV. Therefore, most op amps are operated with a load resistance of a few kilo-ohms which enables an output voltage of not less than ±10 V to be achieved.

Non-inverting amplifier

In the basic amplifier circuit in Figure 4-2, the output voltage is again fed back to the inverting input, but now only partially via a potential divider, R_1-R_2. The values of these resistors ensure that the voltage at the inverting input is only half U_O. This means that if the input to the positive terminal is 1 V, the output voltage must be raised by the amplifier to 2 V to ensure 0 V difference between the inputs. If the ratio R_1:R_2 is altered, different amplification factors are obtained. The amplification factor, A, is calculated from:

$$A = (R_1 + R_2)/R_2 = R_1/R_2 + 1.$$

Figure 4-2.
Basic circuit of an op amp arranged as non-inverting amplifier.

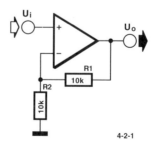

As in the case of the impedance inverter, the amplifier in Figure 4-2 has a very high input resistance and an output resistance of 0 Ω.

Inverting amplifier

The basic amplifier in Figure 4-3 is an inverting type, which means that the output signal is 180° out of phase with the input. If a signal of 1 V is applied to the inverting input, the op amp adjust its output until the difference at its inputs is 0 V. However, here the non-inverting input is at earth potential so that U_O must become more negative to ensure that the inverting input attains earth potential also.

In Figure 4-3, since fairly large resistances are used, the output assumes a level of −1 V. This means that the amplification is −1. As in the previous section, the amplification factor may be altered by giving R_1 and R_2 difference values. Here,

$A = -R_1 / R_2.$

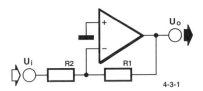

4-3-1

Figure 4-3.
Basic circuit of an op amp arranged as inverting amplifier.

Note that the input resistance of the circuit is equal to the value of R_2 and not, as may be thought, to the sum of R_1 and R_2, since the op amp adjusts the level at the inverting input to earth potential. This means that there is a virtual earth at the junction of the two resistors.

The output resistanceof this circuit is also 0 Ω.

Inverting adder

The inverting adder is really a special form of inverting amplifier. The difference between the two is that the adder has several inputs each of which is applied via a resistor, R_i. The amplification of each of the input signals depends on the value of the relevant input resistor (R_1, the feedback resistor has the same value for whatever input). The equation for amplification, A, is:

$$A = -R_1 / R_{ix},$$

where x is the number of the input.

Figure 4-4.
Basic circuit of an
op amp configured as
adder.

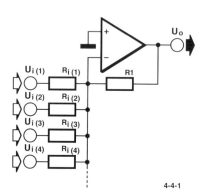

4-4-1

The input resistance of the adder is equal to the relevant input resistor R_{ix}, since the op amp adjust the level at the inverting input to earth potential whichever input is used.

The output resistance of the adder is also 0 Ω.

Inverting adders are used primarily in mixing panels. All input resistors R_i then normally have the same value. Note that the number of inputs may, of course, be much greater than shown in Figure 4-4. In the mixing panel, the various different, discrete signals, processed by the preamplifier and tone control circuits, are added together.

An advantage of this is that none of the signals is attenuated; in fact, depending on the values of the relevant resistors, a degree of amplification is possible. This is

Figure 4–5.
Definitely not the way of
mixing signals.

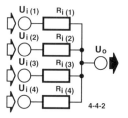

4-4-2

in contrast to the situation when signals are added together with the aid of a few resistors as shown in Figure 4-5. In such a configuration, each of the four signals would be attenuated, so that the effect on the overall signal would be a fourfold attenuation. If in this configuration a signal of 100 mV would be applied to one of the inputs, the output signal level would be only 25 mV. Moreover, this signal would interact with the other inputs, which is definitely not the case when an op amp is used, since then the common junction of the input resistors is always at earth potential.

Differential amplifier

The differential amplifier in Figure 4-6 is a mixture of an inverting and a non-inverting amplifier. It has a positive input (U_{i+}) which is amplified positively and a negative one (U_{i-}) which is inverted, that is, attenuated.

Input signal U_{i-} is amplified according to the equation

$$A- = -R_1 / R_2.$$

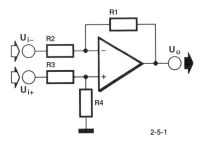

Figure 4-6.
Bsic circuit of an op amp arranged as a differential amplifier.

The situation with input signal U_{i+} is a little more complicated since this is first applied to potential divider R_3-R_4. The overall amplification is determined by R_1, R_2 and the internal resistance of the signal source at the inverting input. The amplification is

$$A_+ = (R_4/R_3 + R_4)(R_1/R_1 + R_2 + R_i),$$

where R_i is the internal resistance of the signal source at the inverting input.

Normally, it may be assumed that R_i is very small and may be ignored. Also, the

47

values of the resistors are normally chosen so that $R_1=R_4$ and $R_2=R_3$. If these assumptions are taken into account, the amplification is

$$A_+ = R/R_2$$
and
$$A_- = -R_1/R_2.$$

These equations show that in a practical circuit, the amplifications of the two sections are equal but of opposite sign.

Instrumentation amplifier

The instrumentation amplifier (see Figure 4-7) is an extended version of the differential amplifier. It needs three op amps and is therefore the most complex of the basic circuits.

Figure 4-7. Configuration of three op amps to form an instrumentation amplifier.

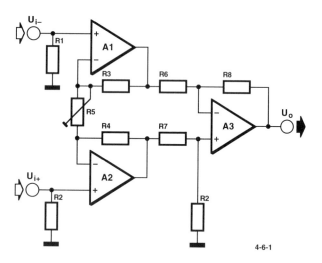

If a balanced signal is to be amplified, a transformer or a balanced amplifier input is needed. The differential amplifier meets the second of these requirements, but its input resistances are somewhat problematic. Moreover, its amplification is not easily controlled, since for that purpose two resistances have to be altered. These difficulties do not arise in the instrumentation amplifier.

In the circuit in Figure 4-7, it is assumed that input voltage U_{i-} is 0 V and U_{i+} is 1 V. Owing to the feedback in A_1, the potential at the junction R_5-R_3 is $U_{i-} = 0$ V.

The amplification of op amp A_2 is that of a non-inverting amplifier and thus depends on the ratio $R_4 : R_5$. Owing to the feedback in this stage, the potential at the junction R_5-R_4 is $U_{i+} = 1$ V.

Op amp A_1, strictly an inverting amplifier, raises U_{i+} according to the ratio of $R_5 : R_3$.

Because of the balanced inputs, signal U_{i-} is processed in the same way, but the two op amp have reversed their roles. That is, A_1 operates as a non-inverting amplifier and A_2 as an inverting one. To obtain a truly balanced amplification, the values of R_3 and R_4 must be identical. The amplification factor, A, is then:

$$A = (2R_3/R_5) + 1.$$

The output voltage is the difference between the voltages at the outputs of A_1 and A_2. This difference is converted into the unbalanced output voltage U_o in the second section of the amplifier. It will be noted that this section is really a differential amplifier based on op amp A_3. In this stage, it is advisable to make R_6 identical to R_7 and R_8 to R_9.

The overall amplification of the instrumentation amplifier is

$$A = ([2R_3/R_5] + 1)(R_8/R_6).$$

The condition for this is that $R_3 = R_4$, $R_6 = R_7$, $R_8 = R_9$.

5. Power supplies

Before a start can be made with designing and constructing practical audio circuits, the design of a power supply is needed. Since most of the circuits in this book are based on operational amplifiers, a symmetrical power supply is required. In this chapter, a suitable mains power supply with a regulated output of ± 15 V that can provide a current of up to 300 mA (depending on the transformer used) will be described.

Requirements

The requirements on a power supply for use in a hi-fi audio installation are stringent. The most important one is probably a clean output voltage free of hum and noise. This is readily achieved nowadays by the use of Type 7815 and 7917 regulator ICs (or their M- or L- versions, for instance, the 78M15). These ensure that the ripple at the output is of the order of not more than a few millivolts. Such a ripple on a music signal would be unacceptable, but in case of the supply voltage this is perfectly all right. After all, this is equivalent to a suppression of residual a.c. by a factor 3000 (or 70 dB). These types of regulator have other advantages as well: they provide current limiting and thermal overload protection, and are proof against short-circuits.

General-purpose power unit

The proposed power supply provides a regulated output voltage of ± 15 V and is suitable for all circuits in the following chapters, with the exception of the output stages in Chapter 12 since these need a higher voltage. Based on a 4.5 watt transformer, the power unit can provide a current of up to 140 mA. That sort of power is more than enough even for large circuits using several quadruple op amps and LEDs. If it is needed for a small circuit only, a much smaller transformer may be used without any problems, since the printed-circuit layout allows transformers of different sizes.

Circuit description

The mains voltage is applied to the transformer primary via fuse F_1. The secondary voltage is 2×15 V (slightly higher at low loads). Bridge rectifier D_1–D_4 and smoothing capacitors C_5 and C_6 produce from this a direct voltage of about 2×20.5 V. The voltage across C_6 is +20.5 V, but that across C_5 is –20 V.

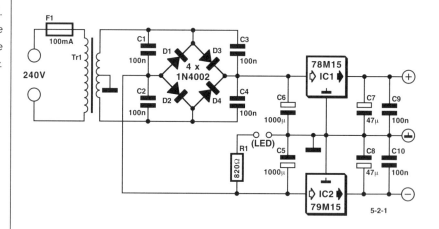

Figure 5-1.
Circuit diagram of the
general-purpose
±15 V power supply.

The reason that the direct voltage is higher than the alternating voltage across the secondary of the transformer is evident from Figure 5-2.

Regulator IC_1 stabilizes the potential across C_6 to +15 V. This voltage is smoothed by capacitors C_7 and C_9. In a similar manner, regulator IC_2 stabilizes the potential across C_5 to –15 V. This voltage is smoothed by capacitors C_8 and C_{10}.

Figure 5-2.
Illustrating why the
direct voltage is higher
than the alternating
voltage at the
secondary of the
mains transformer

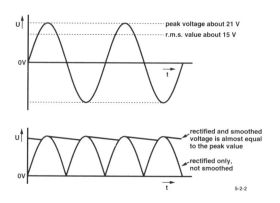

52

Resistor R_1 provides a facility for connecting an on/off indicator LED.

The printed-circuit board whose component layout is shown in Figure 5-3 (track layout at end of this book) was designed to accept a variety of mains transformers rated at 1–10 watts. Simple circuits with not more than five op amps need only a 1-watt transformer; larger ones need a 3-watt type and circuits that contains LEDs as well need more power. Count on a power of 400 mW for each LED. An exception to this is the drive indicator in Chapter 15 in which some of the LEDs are linked in series. Because of that, the circuit needs only a 1-watt transformer although it contains 12 LEDs.

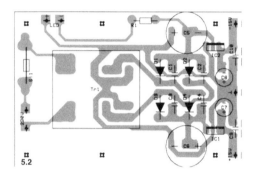

Figure 5-3. Component layout of the printed-circuit board for the ±15 V general-purpose power supply. The track layout is given in the Appendix.

Parts list

Resistors:
$R_1 = 820\ \Omega$

Capacitors:
C_1–C_4, C_9, $C_{10} = 0.1\ \mu F$
C_5, $C_6 = 1000\ \mu F$, 35 V, radial
C_7, $C_8 = 47\ \mu F$, 16 V, radial

Semiconductors:
D_1–$D_4 = 1N4002$

Integrated circuits:
$IC_1 = 7815$ or 78M15
$IC_2 = 7915$ or 79M15

Miscellaneous:

F_1 = fuse, 100 mA, slow with holder

Tr_1 = mains transformer, 2×15 V secondary (for rating see text)

Mains cable

On/off indicator LED (optional)

6. Preamplifiers

The task of a preamplifier is raising a small signal, such as that output by a microphone or a pick-up, to a level of some hundreds of millivolts. To ensure that a preamplifier can cope with a variety of input signals, it must have these properties:
- high-impedance input;
- variable amplification over a large range;
- linear frequency response from 20 Hz to 20 kHz;
- low noise.

Keeping the noise low is the requirement most difficult to attain. Because of that, a few theoretical aspects have to be pondered over.

Noise: causes and remedies

An operational amplifier consists internally of complex circuitry comprising numerous transistors and resistors. All these components generate noise, from the inputs of the op amp, where the so-called input noise originates, to the final transistor stage at the output. The noise generated inside the op amp does not create much of a problem because it is negated largely by the feedback. Imagine that the output voltage of the op amp at a given point of time is a little too high owing to the internally generated noise. Because of the feedback, this offset voltage is applied to the input and thus levelled in the usual way

Input noise is quite a different matter, because this exists at both inputs and is thus treated by the op amp as an input signal. There are various ways and means of designing the amplifier circuit in such a way that the input noise is greatly reduced. One way is, for instance, the reduction of the feedback resistors to very low values, which causes the high-impedance inputs of the op amp to be almost short-circuited. Regrettably, even manufactured consumer equipment sometimes has a preamplifier or input circuit that makes one's hair stand on end. Some examples of this are shown in Figure 6-1.

In circuit 6-1a, the input signal is applied to potentiometer P_1, which enables the signal to be reduced. This is followed by a non-inverting amplifier stage, which raises the signal ×50. So, overall the amplification factor can be varied from 0 to 50.

Figure 6-1.
Various examples of
how not to design the
input stage of a
preamplifier.

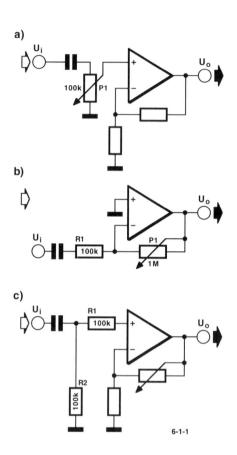

a)

b)

c)

6-1-1

Although this circuit may look all right, it has two serious drawbacks. Firstly, the op amp operates constantly with a ×50 amplification, whereas, say, only ×3 is needed. This causes much unnecessary noise to be generated, since any noise is also amplified ×50. Secondly, imagine that the amplification has been set to ×25, so that potentiometer P_1 is at the centre of its travel, whereupon there are two 50 kΩ impedances at the non-converting input of the op amp: one with respect to earth and the other with respect to the input of the circuit. This means that even when the input signal derives from a low-impedance source, the effect on the op amp is as if it were a high-impedance one. The effect may be reduced by using a 5 kΩ potentiometer instead of a 100 kΩ one. Unfortunately, this would reduce the input impedance of the circuit from 100 kΩ to 5 kΩ, and the op amp would then no longer be suitable for use with signals obtaining from a high-impedance source.Ergo, the circuit in a is not suitable for practical applications.

The circuit in b uses the inverting input of the op amp. The amplification is deter-mined by resistor R_1 and potentiometer P_1. This means that with the values of these components as specified, the amplification may be varied from zero to ten. The input impedance is equal to R_1, that is, 100 kΩ. In this circuit also, the signal applied to the op amp appears to have been derived from a high-impedance source, even though the actual input signal, U_i, is obtained from a low-impedance source. Lowering the values of R_1 and P_1 to, say, 5 kΩ and 50 kΩ respectively ameliorates the problem, but also causes the impedance of the circuit input to be reduced. This would make the preamplifier suitable for use with very-low-impedance signal sources only.

As a basic principle, an inverting op amp is totally unsuitable for use as a pre-amplifier, even though some manufacturers have not acknowledged this.

A totally different picture obtains, however, when inversion in a circuit is need-ed, for in this case the output of a preceding amplifier is low-impedance, and has already been amplified, so that R_1 and P_1 may be given values of, say, 4.7 kΩ and 10 kΩ respectively. Noise is not a problem either because further amplification is not required.

In the circuit of 6-1c, the input signal is applied not only to the op amp via R_1, but also across R_2. The input impedance of the op amp is very high and may be ignored in relation to R_2. This means that the input impedance of the circuit is equal to R_2. Because of the high input impedance of the op amp, resistor R_1 appears not to have any effect. This is, however, not so, because this resistor causes the signal applied to the op amp to be always high-impedance. If, for instance, the signal source at the input has an internal impedance of 5 kΩ, the impedance presented to the op amp is 105 kΩ. If R_1 were omitted, the circuit would be perfectly all right.

It is very odd to consider that resistors as just discussed are found in much equip-ment, although the manufacturers could have saved themselves a little money and at the same have produced a much better equipment if these resistors had been omitted.

In spite of the foregoing, it must be noted that a resistor in series with the input line may have a useful purpose, for instance, in combination with a diode as over-voltage protection. In such a case, however, its value need not be higher than a few hundred ohms.

Two highly usable preamplifier circuits are shown in Figure 6-2. That in 6-2a is a non-inverting amplifier, but here without a resistor in the signal line. This ensures that the internal impedance of the signal source is reflected faithfully at the op amp input and that the signal there is not attenuated. Also, the feedback loop, R_1-P_1, has a fairly low impedance so that the noise at the inverting input of the op amp does

Figure 6-2
Examples of a well-
designed preamplifier
input; the lower one is
preferred.

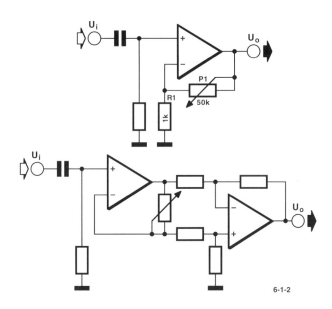

not present any problems. The impedance of the feedback loop should not be reduced further, since in case of the lowest possible amplification, that is, when the effective value of P_1 is zero, the output load consists of just R_1. A value of 1 kΩ is just about the minimum; if this is further reduced, the op amp may not be able to sink sufficient output current and this, of course, limits its dynamic range.

With component values as specified, the amplification may be as high as ×51 with the noise level kept very low. The circuit has a small drawback and that is that its amplification cannot be brought down to 0: unity is lowest. The upper limit of ×51 may be raised slightly by altering the values of the feedback loop components, but this would adversely affect the bandwidth. At a frequency of 20 kHz, the gain is already 1 dB lower than at the middle and low frequencies.

However, for many applications, a control range from unity to ×51 is perfectly acceptable. Should control down to zero be necessary, the circuit in 6-2b must be used. This circuit is a combination of a non-inverting amplifier and a differential amplifier. The circuit works equally well with low-impedance and high-impedance input signal sources, and is, therefore, the one we will use in the construction project in the next section.

General purpose preamplifier

The amplifier whose circuit is shown in Figure 6-3 is suitable for use with low-impedance as well as high-impedance signal sources. Its noise figure is low. The amplification can be varied with P_1, while switch S_1 enables one of two ranges to be selected.

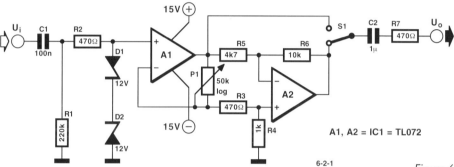

Figure 6-3
Circuit diagram of the general-purpose preamplifier.

Circuit description

The input to the preamplifier is applied to the first stage via C_1 and R_2. Network C_1-R_1 prevent any direct voltage components of the input signal from reaching the input stage. Resistor R_1 also determines the input impedance of the circuit. Diodes D_1 and D_2, in conjunction with R_2, provide overvoltage protection, that is, they prevent voltages higher than 12 V from damaging the input of the op amp.

Operational amplifier A_1 is a non-inverting amplifier whose feedback loop is formed by resistors R_3 and R_4, and potentiometer P_1. The amplification of A_1 can be varies between ×1 and ×35 with P_1.

Operational amplifier A_2 is a differential amplifier, whose amplification is determined by resistors R_5 and R_6. Resistors R_3 and R_4 are also of importance to this stage: they serve as potential divider at the non-inverting input.

With component values as specified, the output signal from A_1 is amplified in A_2 by ×-2.1, while the voltage at the inverting input of A_2 is amplified by ×2.1. When P_1 is turned fully anticlockwise, the amplification is zero, the two input voltages to A_2 are identical, and the amplifier has no output. When P_1 is turned clockwise to increase the amplification, the output of A_1 increases, but the signal at its inverting input remains unchanged.

59

The output of the preamplifier may be taken from A_2 or from A_1, depending on the position of switch S_1. When this switch is in the position shown in the diagram, the overall amplification of the preamplifier covers a range from zero to $\times 72$, but when it is in the upper position, the amplification extends from zero to $\times 35$.

Like C_1, capacitor C_2 prevents any direct voltages from entering or leaving the circuit.

Resistor R_7 determines the output impedance of the preamplifier and also suppresses any tendency of the op amps to oscillate when, for instance, the output is highly capacitive owing to long cable connections.

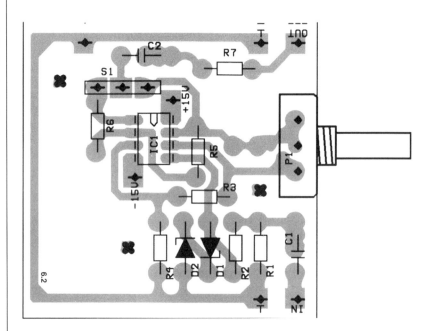

Figure 6-4.
Component layout of
the printed-circuit
board for the general-
purpose preamplifier;
the track layout is
given in the Appendix.

Construction

The preamplifier is best built on the printed-circuit board whose component layout is shown in Figure 6-4. Depending on the application, P_1 may be a potentiometer or a preset: both are catered for on the board. Moreover, a horizontal or a vertical version may be used.

There will normally be no requirement for switch S_1 and therefore the board has provision for this component to be replaced by a simple hardwire link.

In some cases (when, for instance, the circuit is used as a microphone amplifier), it may be that an amplification of $\times 72$ is insufficient. If that is so, the amplification may be increased by giving R_5 a value of 2.2 kΩ, replacing R_4 by a wire bridge, and giving R_3 a value of 1 kΩ. The amplification can then no longer be taken down to zero, but can be varied from $\times 4.5$ to $\times 230$.

This modification may prevent A_1 to be driven to its full extent since the load at the output of this stage has increased. However, the operation of the overall amplifier is not affected by this, since A_2 provides more amplification. It is not advisable to take a signal directly from the output of A_1 and S_1 must therefore be replaced by a permanent wire bridge linking R_6 to C_2.

Components list

Resistors:
R_1 = 220 kΩ
R_2, R_7 = 470 Ω
R_3 = 470 Ω, 1%
R_4 = 1 kΩ, 1%
R_5 = 4.7 kΩ, 1%
R_6 = 10 kΩ, 1%
P_1 = 47 kΩ logarithmic potentiometer (may be preset – see text)

Capacitors:
C_1 = 0.33 μF
C_2 = 1 μF (not electrolytic)

Semiconductors:
D_1, D_2 = zener diodes, 12 V, 500 mW

Integrated circuits:
IC_1 = TL072

Preamplifier with balanced input

A preamplifier with balanced input is best designed on the basis of an instrument amplifier as already discussed in Chapter 5. However, the present design needs rather more amplification than in the earlier example.

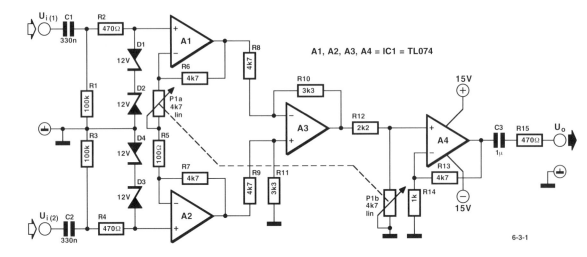

A1, A2, A3, A4 = IC1 = TL074

6-3-1

Figure 6-5.
Circuit diagram of the
preamplifier with
balanced input.

Circuit description

In the circuit diagram in Figure 6-5, the signal is applied to the non-inverting input of op amp A_1 via C_1 and R_2. Capacitor C_1 prevents any direct voltage components on the input signal from entering the circuit. Resistor R_1 determines the input impedance of the circuit. Diodes D_1 and D_2 protect the input stage against overvoltage. The corresponding components at the non-inverting input of A_2 fulfil the same functions. The overall input impedance between the input terminals is the sum of R_1 and R_3, that is, 200 kΩ.

The instrument amplifier, consisting of op amps A_1, A_2, and A_3, provides an amplification of ×2 to ×66. Ideally, the rate of rotation of potentiometer P_1 should be directly proportional to the amplification. To achieve this, the component would have to be a reverse logarithmic model but, since these are difficult to obtain from most electronics retailers, a different solution has been used. This consists of additional control at the output of the instrument amplifier by means of potential divider R_{12}-P_{1b}. The voltage at the junction of these components is amplified ×5.7 in A_4 and then applied to the output terminal via R_{15} and C_3.

The dual gain control with a linear potentiometer ensures an even distribution of the amplification over the range of the potentiometer. It also enables the amplification to be turned down to zero. The overall amplification can be varied in this way from zero to ×260.

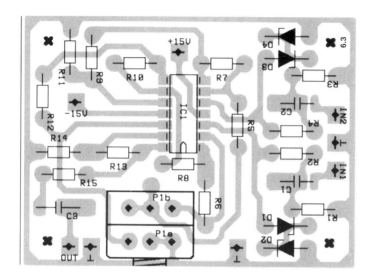

Figure 6-6.
Component layout of
the printed-circuit
board for the preampli-
fier with balanced
input; the track layout
is given in the
Appendix.

Optional modifications

If the preamplifier is used in similar circumstances with only one input signal,
variable amplification is not really necessary, and P_{1a} may then be replaced by
a preset, P_{1b} simply omitted, and R_{12} replaced by a permanent wire bridge.
The printed-circuit board in Figure 6-6 has provision for a standard stereo potentiometer as well as an upright preset. When this modification has been carried out, the amplification can be varied from $\times 12$ to $\times 380$.

If an amplification of $\times 12$ is too high, resistor R_{14} may be omitted and R_{13}
replaced by a permanent wire bridge. This modification makes A_4 ineffective
and the overall amplification is then variable from $\times 2$ to $\times 66$.

Components list

Resistors:
R_1, R_3 = 100 kΩ
R_2, R_4, R_{15} = 470 Ω
R_5 = 100 Ω
R_6, R_7, R_8, R_9 = 4.7 kΩ, 1%
R_{10}, R_{11} = 3.3 kΩ, 1%
R_{12} = 2.2 kΩ
R_{13} = 4.7 kΩ
R_{14} = 1 kΩ
P_1 = 24.7 kΩ stereo, linear potentiometer

Capacitors:
C_1, C_2 = 0.33 μF
C_3 = 1 μF (not electrolytic)

Semiconductors:
D_1–D_4 = zener diode, 12 V, 500 mW

Integrated circuits:
IC_1 = TL074

Gramophone (US: phonograph) preamplifier

Magnetic pickups provide a signal whose level is directly proportional to the velocity of the stylus. This means that high frequencies produce a much higher output than low frequencies of the same amplitude. To obtain a level output over the frequency range, a gramophone preamplifier must have a very special frequency response. The response characteristic is in conformity with the RIAA (Recording Industry Association of America) playback standard with deemphasis time constants of 3180, 318 and 75 microseconds (see RIAA Characteristic in Chapter 3).

The frequency response curve of the preamplifier is shown in Figure 6-7. The characteristic is in conformity with the RIAA standard down to 25 Hz, but below that the response is attenuated additionally by 6 dB/octave by C_3 to suppress any rumble. This arrangement makes a special subsonic filter as provided

Figure 6-7.
Frequency response
curve of the gramo-
phone preamplifier.

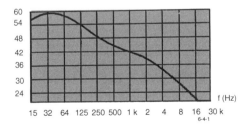

64

in many preamplifiers unnecessary.

Circuit description

In the circuit diagram in Figure 6-8, the input signal is applied to the input amplifier, A_1, via high-pass filter R_1-C_1, which removes direct-voltage and low-frequency components, including rumble, from the signal. Diodes D_1 and D_2 protect the circuit against overvoltage. In contrast to previous circuits, silicon diodes instead of zener diodes are used in this circuit, since the signal output of the cartridge is very small, almost invariably well below the diode threshold voltage of 700 mV.

The input amplifier, A_1, provides frequency-dependent amplification. At low frequencies, the reactance of C_1 is high and therefore ineffectual, whereas at high frequencies it is fairly low. Thus, at high frequencies, resistor R_2 is short-circuited or very nearly so by C_2, so that only R_3 is effective as a feedback loop element. The cut-off frequencies lie at 50 Hz and 500 Hz.

At frequencies up to 50 Hz, the amplification of the input amplifier is linear, and R_9 and R_{10} are then effective in the feedback loop with a total resistance of

Figure 6-8.
Circuit diagram of the gramophone (US: phonograph) preamplifier.

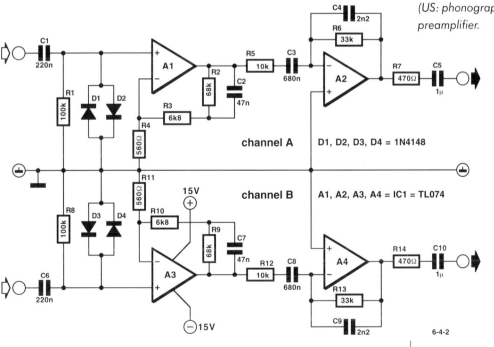

about 90 kΩ. From about 50 Hz onwards, the reactance of C_7 becomes relatively low, which reduces the resistance of R_9 to some extent. This results in the amplification falling off at a rate of 6 dB/octave. At 500 Hz, the reactance of C_7 is so small, that it short-circuits R_9 and only R_{10} remains effective. The amplification then becomes linear again. The overall amplification of the stage is determined by R_4.

The second stage, A_2, is an inverting amplifier whose amplification is determined by R_5 and R_6. Capacitor C_3 and resistor R_5 form a high-pass filter with a cut-off frequency of about 23 Hz. This section is not part of the RIAA correcting network, but serves to suppress rumble and low-frequency feedback.

Capacitor C_4 is effective in the high-frequency part of the RIAA network: together with R_6, it ensures that the amplification above roughly 2 kHz drops at a rate of 6 dB/octave. At frequencies below 2 kHz, the reactance of C_4 is higher than the resistance of R_6, so that the capacitor serves no purpose.

The output signal is applied to the output terminal via R_7 and C_5. The resistor fixes the output impedance at about 500 Ω. Capacitor C_{10} decouples the output for any direct voltage or very low frequency signals.

Amplifiers A_3 and A_4, processing the data of the other stereo channel, function in an identical manner to A_1 and A_2.

Optional modifications

Depending on the cartridge used, some modification(s) may be necessary, for instance, to increase the amplification. If so, the values of R_4 and R_{11} may be reduced, but these should stay within the range 220 Ω to 1.5 kΩ to prevent the equalization frequency response to be adversely affected.

If an additional rumble filter or subsonic filter is used, but a narrowing of the low-pass filter response is not acceptable, the value of C_3 and C_8 may be raised to 1 μF.

Parts list

Resistors:
R_1, R_8 = 100 kΩ
R_2, R_9 = 82 kΩ, 1%
R_3, R_{10} = 8.2 kΩ, 1%
R_4, R_{11} = 680 Ω, 1%
R_5, R_{12} = 10 kΩ, 1%
R_6, R_{13} = 33 kΩ, 1%
R_7, R_{14} = 470 Ω

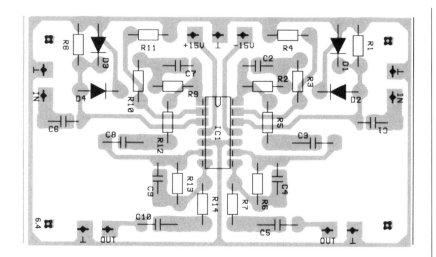

Capacitors:
C_1, C_6 = 0,22 μF, 5%
C_2, C_7 = 0.039 μF, 2.5% (5% just acceptable)
C_3, C_8 = 0.68 μF, 5%
C_4, C_9 = 0.0022 μF, 2.5% (5% just acceptable)
C_5, C_{10} = 1 μF (not electrolytic)

Semiconductors:
D_1–D_4 = 1N4148 (or similar)

Integrated circuits:
IC_1 = TL074

Level matching circuit

The level matching circuit is for use when some equipment provides a signal at too low or too high an impedance. If, for instance, in a hi-fi installation the re-production of the CD player is always higher than that of the tuner, or when the output of the cassette deck is lower than that of the record player, or whatever. Units that may cause problems in this respect are often older units with 5-pin diode sockets. If such a unit is linked via an adaptor to an amplifier with phono sockets, its volume is often too low.

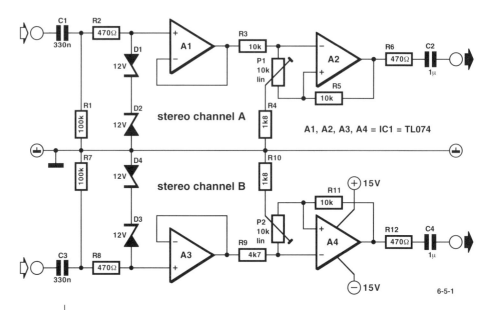

Figure 6-10.
Diagram of the level
matching circuit.

The circuit in Figure 6-10 provides continuous level matching from −16 dB to +16 dB. The gain in the right-hand and left-hand channels of a stereo unit can be adjusted independently with two presets. When these presets are set to their mid-position, the signal remains unchanged (amplification = unity).

Circuit description

The input signal is applied to the input stage, A_1, via high-pass section C_1-R_1 and protection diodes D_1, D_2. The input stage is configured as an impedance converter. The actual level matching is effected by A_2. When P_1 is set fully anti-clockwise, resistors R_3 and R_4 form a potential divider. The signal at the non-inverting input of A_2 is then attenuated by 16 dB referred to the input signal. In this case, A_2 also functions as an impedance converter without any amplification. The resistance of P_1 is then ineffective since, as discussed earlier, an op amp with feedback tends to hold the difference between its two inputs at zero. Consequently, the potentials at the end terminals of P_1 are the same so that no current flows through the component. That being so, the preset cannot possibly have any effect on the amplification.

When, however, P_1 is fully clockwise, R_4 is linked to R_5, whereupon A_2 functions as a non-inverting amplifier with an amplification of 6.5 (determined by R_4 and R_5). There is then no potential division at the non-inverting input of the op amp since again the resistance of P_1 is not effective

When the setting of the potentiometer is somewhere between these two extremes, a combination of attenuation and amplification obtains: which of these predominates depends on the actual setting. When the setting is at exactly midpoint, attenuation and amplification have the same value so that the signal remains unchanged.

The other channel (AS_3 and A_4) functions in the same way, of course.

Optional modifications

The matching range may be altered to some extent by giving R_4 and R_{10} different values. If this value is 10 kΩ, the range is reduced to ±6 dB. This is quite sufficient in most cases and enables a more accurate matching to be obtained.

The matching level can be made manually variable by replacing the presets by a stereo potentiometer which can be linked to the board by three short

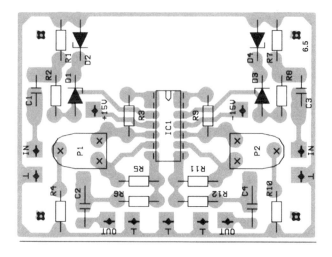

Figure 6-11.
Track layout of the printed-circuit board for the level matching circuit. The component layout is given in the Appendix.

wires.

Components list
Resistors:

$R_1, R_7 = 100 \text{ k}\Omega$

$R_2, R_6, R_8, R_{12} = 470 \text{ }\Omega$

$R_3, R_5, R_9, R_{11} = 10 \text{ k}\Omega, 1\%$

R_4, R_{10} = 1.8 kΩ, 1%
P_1, P_2 = 10 kΩ linear preset

Capacitors:
C_1, C_2 = 0.33 μF
C_3, C_4 = 1 μF (not electrolytic)

Semiconductors:
D_1–D_4 = zener diode, 12 V, 500 mW

Integrated circuits
IC_1 = TL074

7. Filter basics

Filters are of great importance in electrophonics and audio electronics, since they are used to arrange frequency-dependent amplification or attenuation. Rumble filters, tone controls, speech filters, and equalizers, are just a few examples. Filters are also frequently used in effects units. This chapter explains the fundamental principles underlying filters; application circuits will be discussed in the next chapter.

High-pass and low-pass sections

Some of the simplest filter circuits are shown in Figure 7-1. Fundamentally, they both are potential dividers, condsisting of a resistor and a capacitor. The operation of such an *RC* section will be discussed with reference to Figure 7-2.

When an alternating voltage is applied to a capacitor, a phase shift of 90°

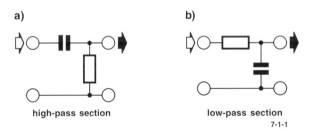

a) **b)**

high-pass section   low-pass section

7-1-1

Figure 7-1. Examples of some of the simplest filter designs.

between the voltage and the consequent current through the capacitor occurs. The largest current flows at the times indicated by the vertical dashed lines, the so-called zero crossings, although at these times there is no voltage across the capacitor. The reason for this is best understood by thinking of the capacitor as a tiny battery that can be charged and discharged very rapidly. The faster the change in voltage takes place, the larger the charging current must be. The largest voltage change takes place at the zero crossings and the current must, therefore, be largest at these points in time.

When the capacitance of the capacitor is doubled, for instance, from 1 μF to 2 μF, the current is also doubled (provided that the applied alternating voltage

Figure 7-2.
The alternating volt-
age applied to a ca-
pacitor and the conse-
quent current through
the capacitor are 90°
out of phase.

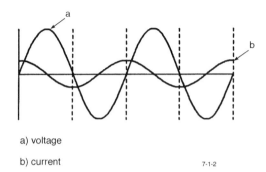

a) voltage

b) current   7-1-2

remains the same. The comparison with a battery is again very apt, because a larger battery needs a larger charging current to become charged in the same time as
a smaller one.

When the frequency of the applied alternating voltage is doubled as in Figure
7-3, the phase shift between voltage and current remains 90°, but the voltage
changes take place twice as fast so that the level of current is also doubled. This
means that the higher the frequency of the applied voltage, the larger the consequent current through the capacitor is (provided the voltage level remains the same).

The ratio of the voltage applied to a capacitor and the consequent current
through the capacitor is the reactance, a quantity similar to resistance. The value of
the reactance, X, in ohms is

$$X = 1/2\pi fC,$$

where f is the frequency in Hz of the applied voltage and C is the capacitance in
farad of the capacitor. This shows that the reactance is inversely proportional to the
frequency of the applied voltage and to the capacitance.

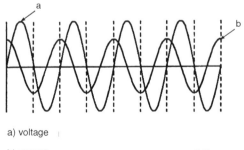

Figure 7-3.
The effect of doubling
the frequency of the
alternating voltage
applied across a
capacitor.

a) voltage

b) current   7-1-3

72

This discussion clarifies the operation of the filters in Figure 7-1. The reactance of the capacitance at low frequencies is much higher than the resistance of the resistor. In the high-pass section, almost the entire applied signal is then short-circuited by the resistor. In the low-pass section, however, the reactance of the capacitor is too high to short-circuit low-frequency signals, which are, therefore, passed virtually unchanged.

Cut-off frequency

Every high-pass filter and low-pass filter has a definite frequency, the cut-off frequency, f_c, at which the reactance of the capacitor is equal to the resistance of the resistor. This frequency in Hz is calculated from

$$f_c = 1/2\pi RC,$$

where R is the resistance and C the capacitance of the filter.

Attenuation at f_c

Since the resistance and reactance are equal at the cut-off frequency, it is clear that in both high-pass and low-pass filters the applied voltage is halved. This would mean that the attenuation is $20\log_{10}0.5 = -6$ dB. However, measurements show that the attenuation in both cases is only 3 dB. This difference is caused by the phase shift between the voltage across, and the current through, the capacitor. At first glance, it may sound wrong, but is not, that the sum of the single voltages across the resistor and capacitor is larger than the applied voltage. This becomes clear from the equation (valid only for series connection of R and C):

$$U_a{}^2 = U_R{}^2 + U_C{}^2,$$

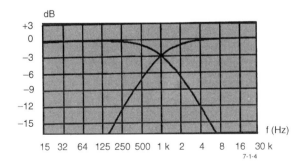

Figure 7-4.
Frequency response curves of a low-pass filter and a high-pass filter.

73

where U_a is the applied voltage, U_R is the voltage across the resistor, and U_C is the voltage across the capacitor.

The frequency-dependent attenuation of a high-pass filter and a low-pass filter is shown in Figure 7-4. It is clear that both filters have their –3 dB cut-off frequency at 1 kHz. Another property of these filters is the steepness or roll-off of the frequency response curve. In the case of a single, called first-order, RC filter this is 6 dB/octave.

Higher-order high-pass and low-pass filters

Filters whose skirts are required to have a roll-off of greater than 6 dB/octave are constructed by cascading a number of *single filters* (i.e., sections). Such cascades are called higher-order filters: the number of sections denotes the order; for example, a three-section high-pass filter is called a third-order high-pass filter.

Figure 7-5 shows the simplest way of obtaining a higher-order filter: two low-pass RC sections have been cascaded. Such arrangements present a few problems

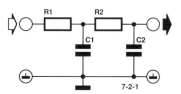

since the sections affect one another. The first section, R_1-C_1 is terminated (loaded) not just by C_1, but also by series network R_2-C_2. The second section has resistor R_1 in series with R_2. To minimize this interaction, the second section, R_2-C_2, must have a higher impedance than section R_1-C_1.

If, for example the elements of the first section are R_1=4.7 kΩ and C_1=0.01 μF, the values of R_2 and C_2 must be of the order of 47 kΩ and 0.001 μF respectively. This causes a further difficulty in that, because of its high impedance, the second section becomes more vulnerable to noise and interference, particularly when the signal voltages are small.

A better and more frequently used circuit that obviates these difficulties is shown

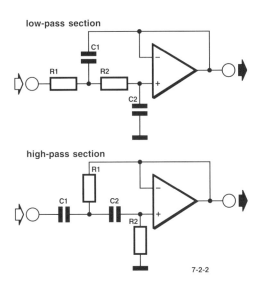

low-pass section

high-pass section

7-2-2

Figure 7-6.
Circuit diagram of an
active 2nd-order filter
that can be used as a
high-pass and as a
low-pass section.

in Figure 7-6. This is an active 2nd-order filter, which may be arranged as a high-pass filter or as a low-pass filter depending on in which branch the resistors and the capacitors are located. If the same values are used for the circuit elements, the response curves in Figure 7-7 ensue.

At f_c, the cut-off frequency determined by R_1-C_1 and R_2-C_2, the attenuation is 6 dB, since each of the sections provides 3 dB at f_c. If the values of any of the circuit elements is altered, the frequency response around f_c changes. It is therefore possible to obtain a given frequency response by giving the circuit elements appropriate values. For instance, Figure 7-8 shows the frequency response of a 2nd order high-pass filter in which R_2 has a value twice that of R_1. The capacitors have identical values. The values of the resistors are calculated from

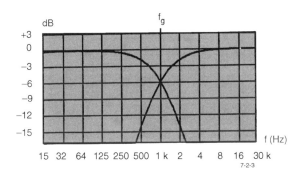

7-2-3

Figure 7-7.
Frequency response
curves of the high-pass
filter or low-pass filter
in Figure 7-6.

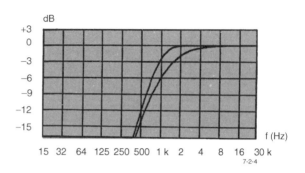

Figure 7-8.
Reponse curves of a
2nd order filter with
$R_1=R_2$ (left) and
$R_2=2R_1$, and $C_1=C_2$.

$$R_1 = 1/\sqrt{2\pi fC}$$

and

$$R_2 = 1/2\sqrt{2\pi f_c C},$$

where f_c is the cut-off frequency and $C=C_1=C_2$. Note that the factor 2 in the original equation has altered to $\sqrt{2}$ in the equation for R_1 and to $2\sqrt{2}$ in that for R_2. The

Figure 7-9.
(a) Curves produced
by high-pass filter
when $R_1=R_2$ (lower)
and $R_2=10R_1$ (upper).
(b) Curve produced by
combination of the
two sections that
produced the
curves in (a).

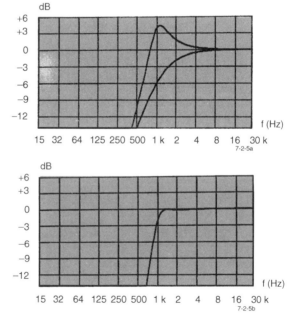

response becomes steeper and levels off quicker in the cut-off frequency region, while the attenuation at the cut-off frequency has again become 3 dB.

Other ratios of R_1 and R_2 give different changes in the frequency response. The lower curve in Figure 7-9 is the response of the high-pass filter when $R_1=R_2$, while the upper curve obtains when $R_2=10R_1$. The hump in the response at the cut-off frequency is made use of in filters of even higher order. If, for instance, the two sections producing the upper and lower curves in Figure 7-9 are formed into a 4th order high-pass filter, the overall response is an appreciable improvement as shown by the curve in the lower diagram in Figure 7-9.

The frequency response of a low-pass filter can be modified in a similar manner by giving C_1 a value ten times that of C_2. The values of the resistors should remain unchanged.

Low-pass and high-pass filters whose frequency response is modified as described are known as Butterworth filters.

Band-pass filters

There are various ways of designing a band-pass filter. Figure 7-10 shows perhaps the simplest: a combination of a high-pass filter and a low-pass filter.

With values as specified for the various components, the cut-off frequencies are at 72 Hz and 7.2 kHz. This simple circuit is suitable for use only when the two cut-off frequencies are well separated, otherwise the two filters affect each other's performance. Also, the roll-off at 6 dB/octave is not particularly good. Much better performance is obtained when the two filters are active higher-order ones.

There are also quite different band-pass filters: special designs that enable a very steep roll-off to obtained with only two capacitors. These are, however, used only when very narrow band operation is required, such as, for instance, in equalizers. These filters are not calculated on the basis of their two cut-off frequencies, but rather on the centre frequency of the pass-band, and the bandwidth or quality factor.

If a circuit as in Figure 7-10 has cut-off frequencies of 72 Hz and 720 Hz, it might be thought that the centre frequency is 396 Hz, i.e, the arithmetic mean. However, since a logarithmic scale is required, the centre frequency, f_m, is calculated from $f_m=\sqrt{(f_{c1}f_{c2})}$, where f_{c1} is the lower cut-off frequency and f_{c2}, the higher. Consequently, the centre frequency is

$$f_m=\sqrt{(72\times720)}=228 \text{ Hz.}$$

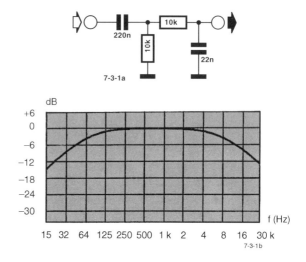

7-3-1a

7-3-1b

*Figure 7-10.
The simplest band-
pass filter consists of a
high-pass section and
a low-pass section.
With component
values as specified,
the frequency
response is as shown
by the curve.*

a)

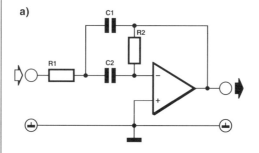

*Figure 7-11.
Circuits of two differ-
ent active band-pass
filters. That in a is
simple and highly suit-
able for some appli-
cations, but may cause
some problems. That
in b is more complex
and may be used in
many applications.*

b)

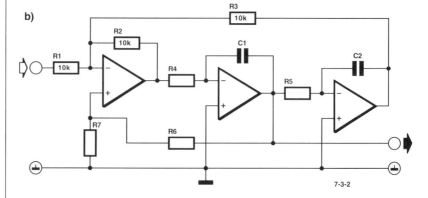

7-3-2

78

The bandwidth, B, is calculated by deducting f_{c1} from f_{c2}, that is

$$B=f_{c2}-f_{c1},$$

which here is 648 Hz.

The quality, Q, of a filter is calculated from the bandwidth and the centre frequency, that is

$$Q=f_m/B,$$

which here amounts to $228/658=0.35$.

The quality factor is therefore a measure of the width of the pass band: the larger Q, the narrower the pass band.

Figure 7-11 shows two band-pass circuits. That in a is fairly simple and uses few components, but has a few drawbacks. If, for instance, a high Q is needed, the circuit will also have a high amplification: $A=-2Q^2$, and this may cause some difficulties with the op amp. Also, the computation of the filter is not easy, since each component affects the quality factor, centre frequency and amplification. Nevertheless, if the Q need not be higher than 5, the circuit is perfectly suitable, particularly in view of its simplicity.

Since, normally, the values of C_1 and C_2 are the same, in the following equations, C $(=C_1=C_2)$ is used.

$$f_m=1/2\pi C\sqrt{(R_1R_2)};$$

$$Q=\sqrt{(R_2/4R_1)};$$

$$A=R_2/2R_1 \text{ or } A=-2Q^2.$$

When Q and f_m are known, R_1 is given a value between 2 kΩ and 10 kΩ, whereupon R_2 and C $(=C_1=C_2)$ are computed as follows.

$$R_2=4R_1Q^2;$$

and

$$C=1/2\pi f_m\sqrt{(R_1R_2)}.$$

The circuit in (b) is rather more complex. In this, the quality factor is determined by potential divider R_6-R_7. A change in the value of these component has no effect on the centre frequency, but has on the amplification. In this circuit, the quality factor and amplification are directly proportional $(A=Q)$. In a, the amplification is directly proportional to the square of Q

In the circuit in b, the centre frequency is determined by R_4, R_5, C_1 and C_2. The resistors as well as the capacitors must have the same value. Then,

$f_m = 1/2\pi RC$,

where $R=R_4=R_5$ and $C=C_1=C_2$.

$Q=A=(R_6+R_7)/3R_7$.

The frequency response of the circuit is shown in Figure 7-12. Each of the curves represents a quality factor; the lowest curve referes to a Q of about 0.3, the next one to a Q of 0.6, the third to one of 1.2, and so: at each successively higher curve the Q value (and the amplification) has been doubled. So, the highest curve refers to a Q of just under 5. Note the difference between these response curves, which all have a pronounced peak at the resonance frequency, and those obtained from a low-pass/high-pass combination, which are normally (relatively) flat over the pass band.

Figure 7-12. Frequency response curves of the filter in Figure 7-11 (b) for various values of Q and A.

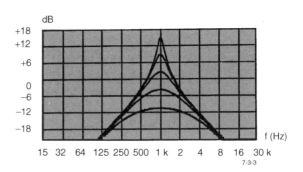

Band-stop filters

The exact opposite of a band-pass filter is a band-stop (or notch) filter, which also may be constructed from a high-pass filter and a low-pass filter. However, in this case, these two filters are not cascaded, but connected in parallel. Owing to their interaction, this is virtually impossible to do with passive RC sections, but is perfectly feasible with active sections.

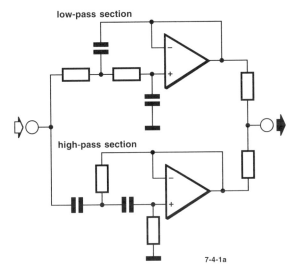

Figure 7-13.
A simple band-stop (notch) filter, composed of a high-pass and a low-pass section, and its frequency response.

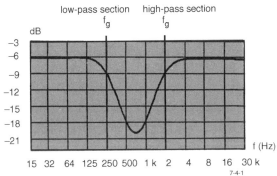

A typical example of such a circuit is shown in Figure 7-13, in which the outputs of the sections are combined by means of two identical resistors. Such an arrangement halves the signal level, which may be obviated by combining the outputs of the sections with an adder as described in Chapter 5. The use of such a circuit lowers the output impedance and counters the attenuation.

A band-stop filter constructed from a high-pass section and a low-pass sections is suitable for use only where a relatively wide frequency range is to be eliminated. For other applications, there are special, more appropriate, designs.

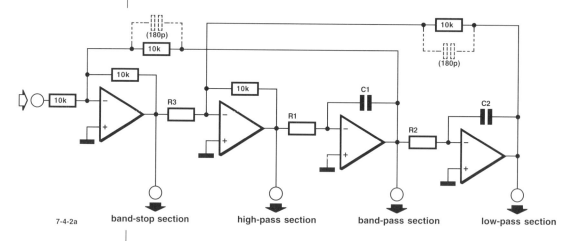

band-stop section   high-pass section   band-pass section   low-pass section

7-4-2a

Figure 7-14. A state-variable filter as shown provides four different outputs. The bandstop response is shown for two values of R_{13}.

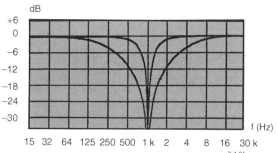

A typical all-round filter is the design in Figure 7-14. This is a state-variable filter, which provides four kinds of filter simultaneously: band-stop, band-pass, high-pass and low-pass; that is, each op amp outputs a different signal. The frequency is determined by equal-value resistors R_1 and R_2, and equal-value capacitors C_1 and C_2. The Q(uality) of the filters is determined by R_3; the resistor and the quality are directly proportional. The higher value of R_3 and Q, the narrower the bandwidth. Resistors R_1 and R_2 may, of course, be replaced by a stereo potentiometer.

Note that in this design the Q has no effect on the amplification.

The capacitors shown in dashed lines are not normally required, but serve to suppress any tendency of the circuit to oscillate.

Double-T filter

The double-T filter, so called because of its shape – see Figure 7-15 – is also a band-stop filter. To obtain the requisite frequency response, the values of resistors R_1 and R_2 must be equal, and R_3 must be half this value. For instance,

$R_1 = R_2 = 10$ kΩ; $R_3 = 5$ kΩ.

The values of capacitors C_1 and C_2 must also be equal, while C_3 must have a value twice as high. For instance,

$C_1 = C_2 = 0.01$ μF; $C_3 = 0.02$ μF.

It will be seen that R_3 and C_3 have non-standard values, and these may be obtained by using a couple of resistors, or a couple of capacitors, as the case may be, in parallel. This enables four equal-value resistors and four equal-value capacitors to be used. Also, in practice, small deviations from their value do not greatly affect the frequency response: for instance, R_3 may well be 4.7 kΩ, and C_3, 0.022 μF.

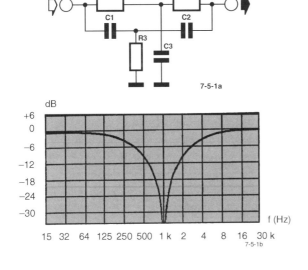

Figure 7-15.
Double-T band-stop filter and its frequency response.

Active double-T filter

To obtain an even narrower frequency response, the filter may use an op amp with feedback. This may be accomplished in various ways, but here we will concern ourselves only with the design in Figure 7-16. In this, the op amp functions as an impedance converter to provide the feedback in the filter. The feedback, and thus the Q of the filter, are controlled with potentiometer P_1. The value of P_1 should preferably be low compared with the filter resistors, so the component does not affect the frequency and other filter properties.

Figure 7-16. Active double-T band-stop filter and its frequency responses. The characteristics are varied with P_1.

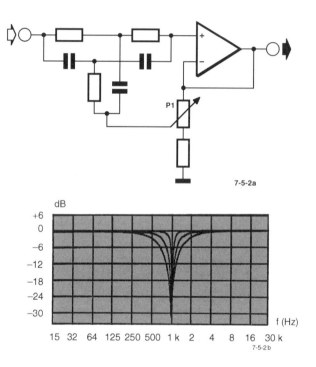

7-5-2a

7-5-2b

Advantages and drawbacks of the double-T filter

The great advantage of the double-T filter is its simplicity and consequently use of only a few components. Unfortunately, it also has some drawbacks:
- the input impedance is low and frequency-dependent;
- the output impedance of the passive versikon is relatively high, and also frequency-dependent;
- all components affect the frequency response and must, therefore, have relatively close-tolerance values;

- the notch frequency cannot be varied with a stereo potentiometer.

All-pass filter

As its name implies, an all-pass filter passes all frequencies. If a music signal is passed through such a filter and we listen to the output, we cannot hear any difference betwen this and the input. If, however, the signals are observed on an oscilloscope, quite a difference will be seen—see Figure 7-17.

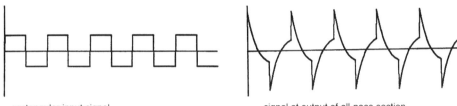

rectangular input signal   signal at output of all-pass section

7-6-1

The changed output of the all-pass filter is the result of a frequency-dependent phase shift, just as happens in a low-pass or high-pass filter. The difference in an all-pass filter is that the signal amplitude remains unchanged over the frequency range. The phase shift is evident in Figure 7-18, which shows the responses of the all-pass filter when the positions of the resistors and capacitors are interchanged.

Figure 7-17. When a square-wave signal (at left) is passed through an all-pass filter, the result we a waveform as shown at the right.

Operation

Let us first consider version a, in which the input signal is applied to the non-inverting input of the operational amplifier via high-pass section R_1-C_1. At the same time, the signal is also applied to the inverting input of the op amp via a potential dividerR_3-R_4, both of which have a value of 10 kΩ.

When the frequency of the input signal is very low, the high-pass section presents such a high impedance that there is virtually no input to the non-inverting amplifier, so that the output of the op amp is almost wholly determined by the input to the inverting section. Since R_3=R_4, the amplification is then −1, which is equivalent to a phase shift of 180°.

When the frequency of the input signal is high, the high-pass section passes virtually the entire signal to the non-inverting amplifier. Since as far this section is con-

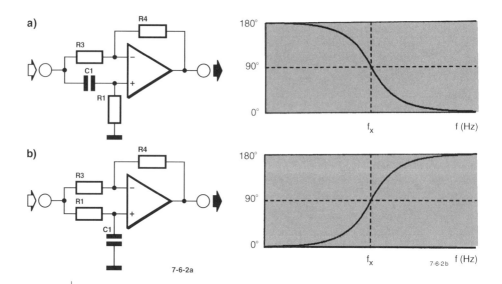

a)

b)

7-6-2a

7-6-2b

Figure 7-18.
When the resistors and
capacitors in an active
all-pass filter are inter-
changed, there is a
phase shift of 180° at
the output.

cerned, R_3-R_4 forms a potential divider to earth, its amplification is 2. However, the amplification of the inverting section remains −1, so that the overall amplification of the op amp is 2−1=1, which is equivalent to a phase shift of 0°.

When the frequency of the input signal lies between the two extremes just discussed, the high-pass section passes only part of the input signal to the non-inverting amplifier. Depending on the actual frequency, R_1 and C_1 not only dampen the signal amplitude, but also cause a phase shift between 0° and 90°. With varying frequency, the overall filter produces a phase shift as shown in Figure 7-18 (top). The amplification is unity throughout.

The operation of the circuit in 7-18b is basically the same, but, owing to their interchanged positions, R_1 and C_1 form a low-pass filter, so that the phase shift is the opposite of that obtained by the circuit in a.

Calculating the frequency

Naturally, an all-pass filter has neither a resonance frequency nor a cut-off frequency. The frequency, f_x, of interest in this type of filter is that at which the phase shift is 90°. This is calculated with the well-known equation

$$f_x = 1/2\pi R_1 C_1.$$

Applications

The all-pass filter finds application most frequently in effects units, more particu-

86

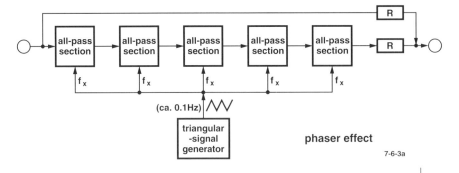

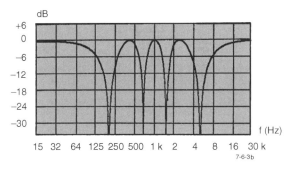

all-pass section ×5 with R blocks

f_x ... f_x ... f_x ... f_x ... f_x

(ca. 0.1Hz)

triangular
-signal
generator

phaser effect

7-6-3a

dB
+6
0
−6
−12
−18
−24
−30

f (Hz)

15 32   64 125 250 500 1 k 2   4   8   16 30 k

7-6-3b

Figure 7-19.
Cascading a number
of all-pass sections
enables variable
phase effects to be
produced.

larly where phase effects are desired. In such units, five or even 10 all-pass filters are cascaded to obtain a frequency-dependent phase shift between 0° and a few hundred degrees. The desired effect is obtained by mixing the original input signal an d the phase-shifted signal. Frequencies shifted by 0°, 360°, 720°, ... are added, whereas frequencies shifted by 180°, 540°, 900°, ... are subtracted—see Figure 7-19. Constant varying of the frequency response of one all-pass section (by varying R_1) causes the highs and lows of the frequency response to shift to and fro, which results in the typical phase effect.

All-pass filters are also used in active (loudspeaker) crossover networks as phase correctors at the crossover frequencies.

Filter in a feedback loop

A filter in the feedback loop of an operational amplifier makes it possible to invert the frequency response, that is, turn attenuation into gain and vice versa—see Figure 7-20.

In the RC network in Figure 7-20a, the capacitor presents a high reactance to

Figure 7-20.
Frequency response of
passive RC network in
a and that when the
RC network is inserted
into the feedback loop
of an op amp (b).

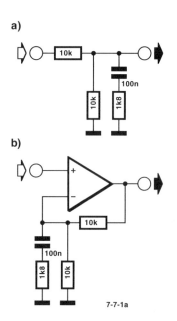

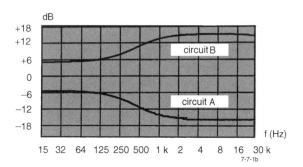

low frequency signals, and can therefore be ignored, so that only the two 10 kΩ resistors function as a potential divider. These resistors cause an attenuation of 6 dB (0.5). At higher frequencies, the capacitor presents a reactance comparable to the resistance of the resistors and so causes additional attenuation. This means that the frequency characteristic falls off. However, the characteristic cannot go down to zero, since the 1.8 kΩ resistor limits the attenuation, whereupon the characteric becomes linear.

The RC network is then inserted into the feedback loop of an op amp as in Figure 7-20b. The larger the attenuation of the filter at a given frequency, the larger the output of the op amp has to be to keep the level at its inverting input close to that at its non-inverting input. This means that attenuation is converted to amplification. The associated frequency response is shown at the top in Figure 7-20.

Similar effects may be produced by different types of filter, even active ones, provided these two conditions are met.

1. The phase shift of the filter must not be so high as to cause the circuit to start oscillating.

2. The output of the filter must not become zero at any frequency, since this would require infinite amplification of the op amp, which is not only senseless, but also greatly increases the risk of the circuit going into oscillation. This is the reason for the 1.8 kΩ resistor in Figure 7-20. Without this, the outpout of the filter would become zero at high frequencies.

Application of a filter in the feedback loop

The use of a filter in the feedback loop finds application most frequently in equalizers and similar tone control circuits. In such circuits, a potentiometer is provided with which it is possible to use the filter passively (as in Figure 7-20a) or in the feedback loop of an op amp (as in Figure 7-20b). With such an arrangement, it is possible to lift or drop a given frequency characteristic at will. A suitable circuit is shown in Figure 7-21.

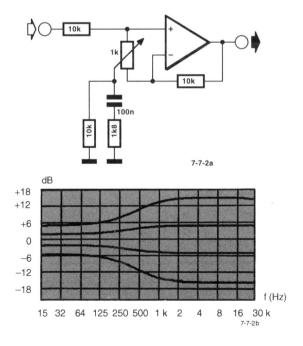

Figure 7-21.
Typical application circuit of a filter in a feedback loop and the consequent response curves.

89

8. Filter circuits

Stereo tone control

The circuit in Figure 8-1 is a straightforward control for adjusting high-frequency (treble) and low-frequency (bass) reproduction as found in many hi-fi installations. Nevertheless, it has a few noteworthy properties. Two isolated operational amplifiers are used for the treble and bass control. This means that for a stereo version four op amps are needed. The number of passive components is, however, low. In each channel, only two capacitors, C_2, C_3 and C_6, C_7 respectively, are needed for the frequency control.

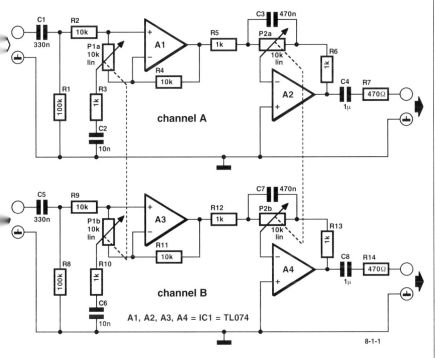

Figure 8-1.
Circuit diagram of the simple stereo tone control.

Figure 8-2.
Frequency response
curves of the tone
control circuit.

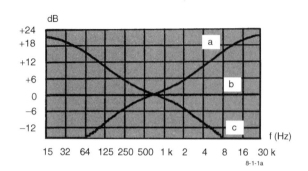

Circuit description

The description in this section is based on (left-hand) channel A: operation of (right-hand) channel B is, of course, identical, but the component identification is different.

The input signal is decoupled by R_1-C_1 and then applied to op amp A_1. This stage provides high-frequency control and is very similar to the level matching circuit in Figure 6-10. In the present circuit, capacitor C_2 limits the control to the treble (high) frequencies.

When potentiometer P_1 is turned fully anticlockwise, R_2 and C_2 form a low-pass section at the inverting input of the op amp. Resistor R_3 provides the maximum attenuation in the highest frequency range.

When P_1 is turned fully clockwise, R_4 and C_2 form a low-pass section in the feedback loop that provides a completely different frequency response, in which the high frequencies are lifted.

The bass control is provided by A_2. If we ignore capacitor C_3, the stage becomes a standard inverting amplifier. When potentiometer P_{2a} is turned fully anticlockwise, it forms a series network with resistor R_5. The amplification of the stage is then well below unity.

When P_{2a} is turned fully clockwise, it forms a series network with resistor R_6. The amplification is then appreciably greater than unity.

When the wiper of P_{2a} is anywhere between the extreme positions, one part of the potentiometer resistance is in series with R_5, and the other with R_6.

Capacitor C_3 short-circuits P_{2a} at midrange and treble frequencies, so that the potentiometer acts on bass frequencies only.

The signal is applied to the output of the circuit via R_7 and C_4.

Input impedance

In contrast to most other circuits, there is an impedance converter and an overvolt-

92

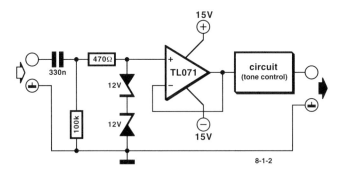

Figure 8-3.
Impedance converter for use when the output impedance of the tone control does not match the input of the unit it is connected to.

age protection at the input. This ensures that the input impedance is neither too high nor frequency-dependent. At bass frequencies below about 500 Hz, it amounts to about 47 kΩ. At higher frequencies, it drops to around 9 kHz, depending on the setting of the treble control.

If the tone control precedes a preamplifier or level matching unit, the input impedance will not pose any problems. However, if it is connected directly to a CD player, cassette deck or similar unit, it is advisable to connect it via an impedance converter as shown in Figure 8-4.

If the tone control is needed as a mono(phonic) device only, the components for the second channel may, of course, be omitted. However, resistors R_8, R_9, and R_{11}, must be replaced by wire bridges. Also, the stereo potentiometers should then be

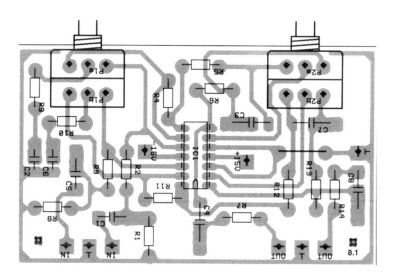

Figure 8-4.
Component layout side of the printed-circuit board for the tone control. The track side is given in the Appendix.

replaced by mono types. Finally, the inverting input of A_4 must be linked to the output of A_4 to prevent any tendency of the unused op amps to oscillate.

Components list:
Resistors:
R_1, R_8 = 100 kΩ
R_2, R_4, R_9, R_{11} = 10 kΩ, 1%
R_3, R_5, R_6, R_{10}, R_{12}, R_{13} = 1 kΩ, 1%
R_7, R_{14} = 470 Ω
P_1, P_2 = stereo potentiometer, 2×10 kΩ, linear

Capacitors:
C_1, C_5 = 0.33 μF
C_4, C_8 = 1 μF (not electrolytic)
C_2, C_6 = 0.01 μF, 5%
C_3, C_7 = 0.47 μF, 5%

Integrated circuits:
IC_1 = TL074

Stereo midrange-frequency tone control

The circuit in Figure 8-5 is not a stand-alone unit, but an extension to the tone control discussed in the previous section (Figure 8-1). The two circuits are simply connected in series. The result is a three-way tone control, which has a wider control range than the two-way unit (for example, by lifting the bass and treble and simultaneously lowering the midrange frequencies).

In the circuit in Figure 8-5, adjusting P_{1a} determines how much of the resistance of this control is in series with R_1 and how much with R_2. Depending on the setting of the control, inverting op amp A_1 provides a gain between –20 dB and +20 dB.

At high frequencies, capacitor C_3 has a very low impedance and short-circuits the potentiometer. This means that the circuit functions only as far as bass and midrange frequencies are concerned. However, capacitor C_2 and resistors R_3 and R_4 prevent the circuit acting on the bass frequencies. This is because at these frequencies C_2 has a high impedance, so that R_3 and R_4 determine the amount of feedback instead of the potentiometer. The overall result is that the circuit controls midrange frequencies only.

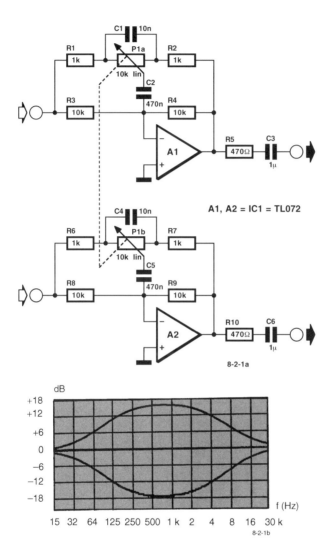

Figure 8-5.
Circuit diagram and
frequency response
curves of the midrange
tone control extension.

The operation of the circuit for the other channel is, of course, identical to that just discussed, only the component identifications are different.

Connecting up

The midrange tone control is linked to the bass/treble control as shown in Figure 8-7. In the bass/treble control circuit, capacitors C_4 and C_8, as well as resistors R_7 and R_{14}, must be replaced by wire bridges.

Figure 8-6.
Setup of the bass/
treble tone control
and the midrange
control.

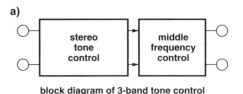

a)

block diagram of 3-band tone control

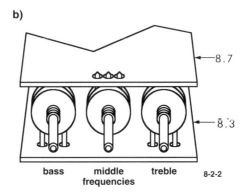

b)

bass   middle   treble   8-2-2
frequencies

It is advisable to arrange the three tone controls as shown in the lower diagram of Figure 8-7.

Input impedance

As in the bass/treble control, the input of the midrange tone control circuit is provided with an impedance converter and overvoltage protection network. This is the reason that capacitors C_4 and C_8, as well as resistors R_7 and R_{14}, in the bass/treble control circuit must be replaced by wire bridges: the midrange control circuit is then provided directly with the the output of the relevant op amp. If the midrange control unit is used with a circuit other than that in Figure 8-1, the relevant components at the output of that circuit must also be replaced by a wire bridge. If the midrange control unit is to function as the input for the signal, it may be necessary to precede it with an impedance converter as discussed earlier with the bass/treble unit.

The midrange control unit may also be constructed as a mono(phonic) unit: R_6–R_{10}, C_4–C_6, and P_{1b} are then superfluous. Resistor R_9 must be replaced by a wire bridge, while P_1 may be a mono potentiometer. The other components mentioned can simply be omitted.

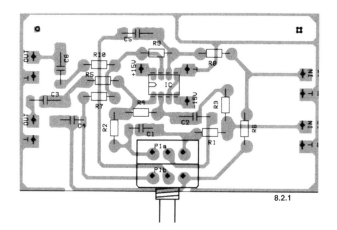

Figure 8-7.
Component layout of
the printed-circuit
board for the
midrange frequency
control unit. The track
side is given in the
Appendix.

Components list

Resistors:
R_1, R_2, R_6, R_7 = 1 kΩ, 1%
R_3, R_4, R_8, R_9 = 10 kΩ, 1%
R_5, R_{10} = 470 Ω
P_1 = stereo potentiometer, 2×10 kΩ, linear

Capacitors:
C_1, C_4 = 0.01 μF, 5%
C_2, C_5 = 0.47 μF, 5%
C_3, C_6 = 1 μF (not electrolytic)

Integrated circuits:
IC_1 = TL072

Noise filter

The simplest way of eliminating noise on a signal is to filter out the high frequencies with a low-pass filter, since by far the largest part of what we hear as noise lies in the frequency range above 10 kHz. This has the serious drawback, however, that the high frequency constituents of the signal are also eliminated. Nevertheless, the low-pass filter offers a very suitable compromise in many cases.

Figure 8-8.
Frequency response of
a noise filter with a
cut-off frequency at
10 kHz.

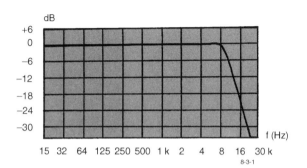

8-3-1

As an example, v.h.f. radio broadcasts do not contain any frequencies above 15 kHz. The noise that is audible during bad reception (weak signal) lies for a large part above that frequency. This means that the noise can be reduced appreciably by the use of a 15 kHz low-pass filter without the broadcast signals being affected. As a bonus, the 19 kHz pilot carrier transmitted by all broadcast stations is also suppressed or at least attenuated. Owing to its frequency, this tone cannot be heard by most people, but it can cause intermodulation when a broadcast is recorded on a cassette tape, which is audible as additional noise or hiss. The attenuation of the pilot tone is not normally necessary, however, because all good tuners and cassette decks have a built-in 19 kHz notch filter.

Also, a noise filter may prove very beneficial when it is used with old recordings from the 1960s and early 1970s. In those days, the available technology made it virtually impossible to record frequencies above 10 kHz. Consequently, use of a 10 kHz low-pass filter may work wonders not only with old cassette or reel-to-reel tapes, but also with vinyl records of those years.

Another application for a noise filter lies in its use with some musical instruments. For instance, the upper frequency range, that is above, say, 8 kHz, of a bass

Figure 8-9.
Circuit diagram of a
typical noise filter.

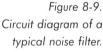

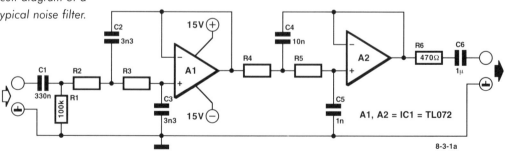

8-3-1a

98

drum or a bass guitar may be cut off without any detriment to the instrument's sound. The same applies to some keyboard sounds. Also, in the case of distorted E-string guitars, frequencies above 8 kHz are very disturbing, since they make the guitar sound scratchy. This is why most guitar amplifiers have a frequency range that is cut off above about 6 kHz. An 8 kHz low-pass filter can eliminate not only any noise, but also suppress most of the scratchiness in the sound. So as to make a noise filter optimally usable for a given application, it is essential that its cut-off frequency be changeable by means of altering the value of certain components.

Circuit description

The diagram of a typical noise filter is shown in Figure 8-9. The input signal is decoupled by R_1-C_1 and applied to the non-inverting input of operational amplifier A_1. Operational amplifiers A_1 and A_2 form a fourth order active low-pass filter. The values of capacitors C_2–C_5 are chosen to obtain a Butterworth filter characteristic. In this type of filter, the amplification remains constant right up to the cut-off frequency, after which it drops fairly rapidly. The fundamentals of such a filter were discussed in 'Higher-order high-pass and low-pass filters' in Chapter 7.

The values of resistors R_2–R_5 are identical, and depend on the wanted cut-off frequency.

Any direct voltage remaining at the output is blocked by capacitor C_6. Resistor R_6 determines the output impedance and also suppresses any tendency of the output stage to oscillate owing to the capacitance of possibly long cables at the output.

Input impedance

At low frequencies within the passband of the filter, the input of the filter is determined by R_1. With rising frequency, the input impedance drops gradually to the value of R_2. The output impedance of the preceding circuit should be no more than a quarter of the value of R_2. If this is not so, an impedance converter as for instance shown in Figure 8-4 should be used so as not to degrade the properties of the filter.

Components list

Resistors:
R_1 = 100 kΩ
R_2–R_5 = see below, 1%
R_6 = 470 Ω

Capacitors:
C_1 = 0.33 µF

C_2, C_3 = 0.0033 μF, 5% (2.5% preferred)
C_4 = 0.01 μF, 5% (2.5% preferred)
C_5 = 0.001 μF, 5% (2.5% preferred)
C_6 = 1 μF (not electrolytic)

Integrated circuits:
IC_1 = TL072

* The value of resistors R_2–R_5 depends on the wanted cut-off frequency and is calculated with the equation
$$R_{2-5} = X/f_c \ [\Omega],$$
where $X = 1/2\pi(C_2C_3C_4C_5)^{1/4}$ (capacitor values in farad), and f_c is the cut-off frequency in hertz. With values of capacitors as specified in Figure 8-9, the value of $X = 49.27\times10^6$. The correlation between some standard resistor values and the resulting cut-off frequency (with the capacitor values in Figure 8-9 retained) are:

R_2–R_5 (kΩ)	f_c (kHz)	comments
47	1.05	
39	1.26	
33	1.49	
27	1.82	
22	2.24	
18	2.74	
15	3.28	limit of speech intellegibility
12	4.11	
10	4.93	
8.2	6.01	
6.8	7.24	
5.6	8.80	suitable for bass instruments
4.7	10.5	
3.9	12.6	
3.3	14.9	suitable for v.h.f. receivers
2.7	18.2	
2.2	22.4	ultrasonic filter
1.8	27.4	
1.5	32.8	

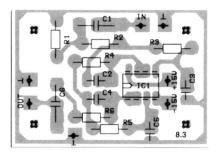

Figure 8-10.
Component layout of
the printed-circuit
board for the noise
filter. The track side of
the board is given in
the Appendix.

Rumble filter

A frequently encountered problem in record players (US: gramophone) is rumble: a low-frequency (for most people subsonic) noise, usually of indeterminate pitch, caused by the physical vibration of the turntable (or even of the building in which the recording was made). Equipment without a rumble filter will, of course, reproduce this noise at an amplified level. Although it is generally inaudible, it nevertheless loads the amplifier and loudspeakers and, in severe cases, can damage these.

A rumble filter to reduce the severity of the amplified noise is normally a fourth-order high-pass filter with cut-off frequency at around 30 Hz (most people cannot hear frequencies below this point).

Circuit description

The circuit diagram of a typical rumble filter is shown in Figure 8-11. The fourth-order, active high-pass filter is composed of two operational amplifiers, capacitors C_1–C_4 and resistors R_1–R_4. As in the noise filter, the cut-off frequency may be altered, but in this filter not by changing the value of the resistors, but that of the

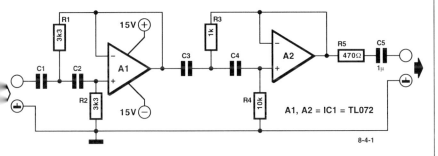

Figure 8-11.
Circuit diagram of a
typical rumble filter.

101

Figure 8-12.
Frequency response of
the rumble filter with a
cut-off frequency of
50 Hz.

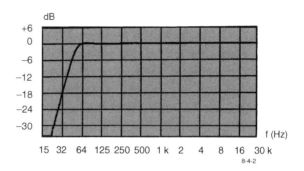

capacitors, C_1–C_4. The values of resistors R_1–R_4 are chosen to give a Butterworth frequency response characteristic. The fundamentals of such a filter were discussed in 'Higher-order high-pass and low-pass filters' in Chapter 7. The filter is terminated in network R_5-C_5, whichblocks any residual direct voltage at the output and determines the output impedance.

Input impedance

Like the noise filter, the rumble filter probably does not require to be preceded by an impedance converter, provided the following conditions are met. The preceding circuit should have an output impedance of not greater than 1 kΩ. Any capacitor at the output of the preceding circuit must be short-circuited to prevent it changing the cut-off frequency of the rumble filter (it would be in series with C_1). In all other cases, an impedance converter is required at the input of the rumble filter.

Components list

Resistors:
R_1, R_2 = 3.3 kΩ, 1%

Figure 8-13.
Component layout of
the printed-circuit
board for the rumble
filter. The track side is
given in the Appendix.

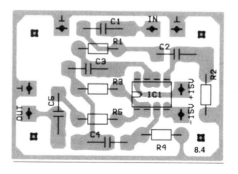

$R_3 = 1\ k\Omega,\ 1\%$
$R_4 = 10\ k\Omega,\ 1\%$
$R_5 = 470\ \Omega$

Capacitors:
$C_1–C_4$ = *see below. 5% (2.5% preferred)
$C_5 = 1\ \mu F$ (not electrolytic)

Integrated circuits:
IC_1 = TL072

* The value of capacitors $C_1–C_4$ depends on the wanted cut-off frequency and is calculated with the equation

$$C_{1-4} = 1/Xf_c\ \text{[F]},$$

where $X = 2\pi(R_1R_2R_3R_4)^{1/4}$ (resistor values in ohms), and f_c is the cut-off frequency in hertz. With values of resistors as specified in Figure 8-11, the value of $X = 20.297 \times 10^3$. The correlation between some standard capacitor values and the resulting cut-off frequency (with the resistor values in Figure 8-11 retained) are:

$C_1–C_4$ (μF)	f_c (Hz)	comments
10	4.93	
6.8	7.24	
4.7	10.5	
3.3	14.9	suitable for use with record player
2.2	22.4	suitable for use with record player
1.5	32.8	
1.0	49.3	
0.68	72.4	
0.47	105	
0.33	149	
0.22	224	
0.15	328	
0.1	493	

Speech filter

In the reprodution of speech signals, the presence range of 1000–4000 Hz is of special interest, since the harmonics contained in that range are of the greatest importance for good intelligibility. The characteristic tones of individual voices are also contained in this range.

Figure 8-14.
Circuit diagram of a
typical speech filter.

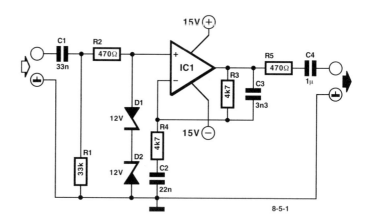

The speech filter in Figure 8-14 provides a slight preemphasis of the presence range of about 2000–6000 Hz. The frequency range is rather wider than strictly required in a presence filter, because if it were narrower the preemphasis would make the speech sound rather shrill.

The filter contains an additional high-pass section which provides a slight attenuation of the fundamental frequencies of the speech. This section is particularly useful in combatting the muffled murmuring so often present in the reproduction of public-address (PA) installations, discotheque equipment, or live-band equipment, in which the bass frequencies have been overemphasized.

Experimenting (electric) guitar players may connect the speech filter to the input of the guitar amplifier. The sound of the guitar then contains rather more high frequencies and becomes rather more transparent.

Circuit description

Network R_1-C_1 at the input of the filter—see Figure 8-14—serves not only as decoupling element for direct voltages, but also as high-pass section. Its cut-off frequency

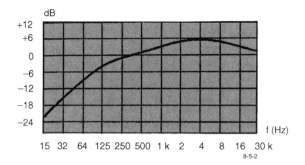

Figure 8-15.
The overall frequency
response of the speech
filter.

is around 150 Hz. The fundamental frequencies contained in speech signals, which may be as low as 100 Hz, are thus slightly attenuated.

Diodes D_1 and D_2, and resistor R_2, form an overvoltage protection network for the input of the op amp. Because of this network, which is used in several other circuits in this book, and the high input impedance, determined by R_1, the speech filter can be used with almost any other appropriate equipment.
Amplifier IC_1, in conjunction with resistors R_3 and R_4, and capacitors C_2 and C_3, provides frequency-dependent feedback. At low frequencies, C_2 has a high reactance and the whole output signal is then fed back. The amplification is then unity. At somewhat higher frequencies in the presence rang e, C_2 has a relatively low reactance, causing the amount of feedback to be determined by potential divider R_3-R_4. The amplification is then 2 (gain=6 dB). At even higher frequencies, though, C_3 short-circuits R_3, whereupon the amplification is brought back to unity.

Optional alterations
In some cases, it may prove necessary to alter the filter operation to some extent. For instance, when in spite of the high-pass section there is still muffled murmuring, it may prove helpful to reduce C_1 to 0.022 μF. The complete removal of C_3 may also be beneficial in some cases. Without this capacitor, the high and middle-high frequencies, which contain the sibilants, are given a boost.

Components list
Resistors:
R_1 = 33 kΩ, 1%
R_2, R_5 = 470 Ω
R_3, R_4 = 4.7 kΩ, 1%

Figure 8-16.
Component layout of
the printed-circuit
board for the speech
filter. The track side is
given in the Appendix.

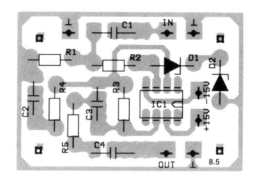

Capacitors:
C_1 = 0.033 μF, 5%
C_2 = 0.022 μF, 5%
C_3 = 0.0033 μF, 5%
C_4 = 1μF (not electrolytic)

Integrated circuits:
IC_1 = TL071

Presence control

Presence is a quality of realism and aliveness in a reproduced sound. Sometimes, it is desired to increase the presence of a certain musical instrument or to improve intelligibility, and for this purpose many mixing consoles and amplifiers have a dedicated presence control. Many microphones used for singing and loudspeakers provide much, sometimes too much, emphasis on the presence range.

Most commercial presence controls have the drawback that they provide emphasis, but no deemphasis, on the presence range. The control described here provides both. The presence range may be adjusted between −15 dB and +15 dB. When the control is in its centre position, the signal is not affected.

Circuit description
The circuit diagram of the presence control is shown in Figure 8-17. The input stages consist of an impedance convertor and overvoltage protection network. The control proper is provided by the filter formed by op amps A_3 and A_4.in conjunction with resistors R_5 and R_6, and capacitors C_2 and C_3. In contrast to the other filters described so far, this one has neither input nor output, but is merely coupled to

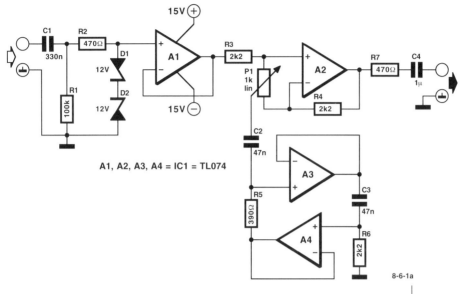

A1, A2, A3, A4 = IC1 = TL074

8-6-1a

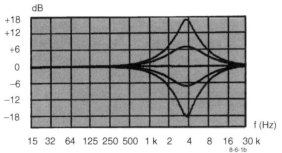

8-6-1b

Figure 8-17.
Circuit diagram of a
typical presence
control and the fre-
quency responses
attainable with it.

the remainder of the circuit by capacitor C_2.

The filter forms a frequency-dependent impedance to earth, which has a minimum value at about 3500 Hz. However, at low and high frequencies, it has a much
higher impedance. Control P_1 enables the filter to function, in conjunction with R_3,
as a potential divider, or, together with R_4, to form a feedback element to provide a
complementary frequency response.

Components list
Resistors:
$R_1 = 100 \text{ k}\Omega$
$R_2, R_7 = 470 \ \Omega$

107

Figure 8-18.
Component layout of
the printed-circuit
board for the presence
control. The track side
is given in the
Appendix.

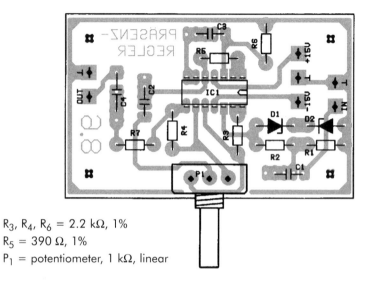

R_3, R_4, R_6 = 2.2 kΩ, 1%
R_5 = 390 Ω, 1%
P_1 = potentiometer, 1 kΩ, linear

Capacitors:
C_1 = 0.33 μF
C_2, C_3 = 0.047 μF, 5%
C_4 = 1μF (not electrolytic)

Semiconductors:
D_1, D_2 = zener diode, 12 V, 500 mW

Integrated circuits:
IC_1 = TL074

Special filter for electric guitars

Most bands that use a public address (PA) system, take the output of the guitar from the guitar amplifier via a microphone. In this way, the characteristic sound of the guitar amplifier, which is predominantly determined by the frequency response of the loudspeakers, is retained in the PA reproduction. Nevertheless, the sound of an electric guitar from a PA system is seldom as good as that directly from the guitar amplifier. This is caused primarily by the frequency response of the microphone and of the PA loudspeakers. There are many additional resonances and attenuations that often cause the guitar to sound unpleasantly shrill or muddy. Anyone who has ever tried to record a piece of music by microphone from a loudspeaker, instead of via a cable, knows the problem, because the effect is exactly the same.

Of course, this problem may be obviated by taking the signal directly from the output socket of the guitar amplifier or from a preceding effects unit. Unfortunately, the special sound of the guitar is then not passed on to the PA system. And, there is another problem.

The frequency response of the guitar amplifier rolls off steeply from about 6 kHz. Without the high-frequency attenuation, the guitar would sound very scratchy when it is played in conjunction with a distortion unit. Moreover, with direct pick-up, the low frequencies would be emphasiszed more than the higher ones.

It is clear that several frequency corrections are necessary. A good equalizer often gives very satisfactory results, but better is a special filter as described below.

The special filter attenuates the high frequencies with a fifth-order (30 dB per octave) low-pass filter. Bass frequencies below 200 Hz are attenuated rather less severely at 6 dB per octave . The filter also provides individual tone setting via a switched high-frequency emphasis, and a narrow-band midrange deemphasis with variable frequency.

In virtually all cases, the special filter provides an excellent guitar sound via the PA system, but there is a downside to this: the original guitar sound gets lost.

Circuit description

In the circuit in Figure 8-19, impedance converter A_1, in conjunction with resistor R_1, provides a high input impedance. So as to enable an electric guitar to be linked in directly, the input impedance is high by most standards: 1 MΩ.

Diodes D_1 and D_2, together with resistor R_2, form an overvoltage protection network. If this is found superfluous, the diodes may be omitted and R_2 replaced b y a wire bridge.

The output of the impedance converter is split into two: one branch is applied to the bypass output via R_3 and C_2, to which the guitar amplifier is connected.

The filter circuit proper begins with high-pass filter R_4-C_3, which attenuates bass frequencies below about 200 Hz.

The output of the high-pass section is applied to amplifier A_2, which has frequency-dependent feedback. The amplification at low frequencies is unity. From about 500 Hz onwards, capacitor C_4 comes into action, provided switch S_1 is closed. The amplification then rises until at about 2 kHz it is levelled off by resistor R_6, and remains constant after that.

When switch S_1 is opened, A_2 functions as an impedance converter. Resistor R_7 at the output of A_2 serves two purposes. First, in conjunction with capacitor C_5, it

Figure 8-19.
Circuit diagram of the
special filter for
electric guitars.

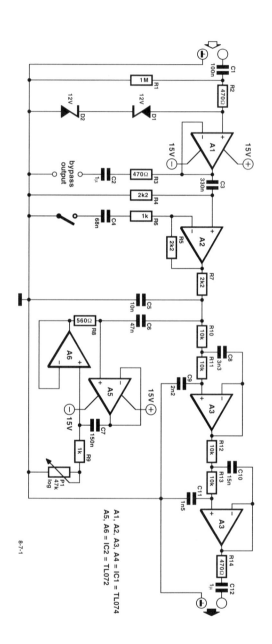

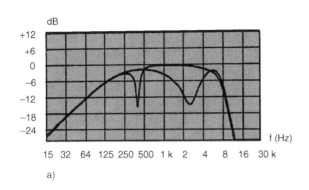

a)

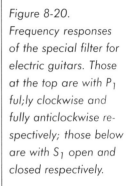

Figure 8-20.
Frequency responses
of the special filter for
electric guitars. Those
at the top are with P_1
ful;ly clockwise and
fully anticlockwise re-
spectively; those below
are with S_1 open and
closed respectively.

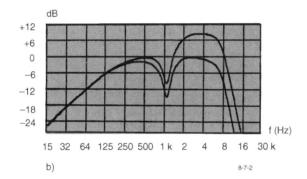

b)   8-7-2

forms a low-pass filter with a cut-off frequency of 6 kHz, and, second, with the fil-ter at C_6, it forms a frequency-dependent potential divider.

The filter at C_6 consists of that capacitor and R_8, C_7, R_9, P_1, A_5 and A_6. In es-sence, it form a series resonant circuit to earth. In conjunction with R_7, it provides about 12 dB attenuation over a narrow band of midrange frequencies. The centre frequency of this band can be set between 370 Hz and 2500 Hz with P_1. It should be noted that this also affects the Q factor of the filter, that is, the bandwidth of the range of frequencies being attenuated.

The last two stages, A_3 and A_4, constsitute a fourth-order low-pass filter with a cut-off frequency of about 6 kHz. The values of capacitors C_8–C_{11} are chosen to improve the filter to a fifth-order type with optimal frequency response.

After the guitar signal has passed through the various single filters, it is applied to the second output, the filter output, from where it can be applied to the input of a PA system.

*Figure 8-21.
Component layout of
the printed-circuit
board for the special
filter for electric
guitars. The track side
is given in the
Appendix*

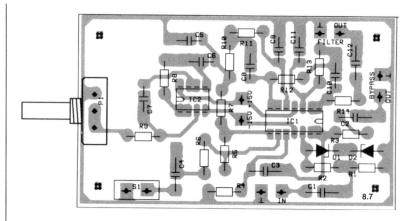

Components list

Resistors:

$R_1 = 1\ M\Omega$

$R_2, R_3, R_{14} = 470\ \Omega$

$R_4, R_5, R_7 = 2.2\ k\Omega, 1\%$

$R_6, R_9 = 1\ k\Omega, 1\%$

$R_8 = 560\ \Omega$

$R_{10}, R_{11} = 10\ k\Omega, 1\%$

$R_{12}, R_{13} = 4.7\ k\Omega, 1\%$

$P_1 = 47\ k\Omega$ logarithmic potentiometer

Capacitors:

$C_1 = 0.1\ \mu F$

$C_2, C_{12} = 1\ \mu F$ (not electrolytic)

$C_3 = 0.33\ \mu F, 5\%$

$C_4 = 0.068\ \mu F, 5\%$

$C_5 = 0.01\ \mu F, 5\%$

$C_6 = 0.047\ \mu F, 5\%$

$C_7 = 0.15\ \mu F, 5\%$

$C_8 = 0.0033\ \mu F, 5\%$

$C_9 = 0.0022\ \mu F, 5\%$

$C_{10} = 0.015\ \mu F, 5\%$

$C_{11} = 0.0015\ \mu F, 5\%$

Semiconductors:
D_1, D_2 = zener diode 12 V, 500 mW

Integrated circuits:
IC_1 = TL074
IC_2 = TL072

Miscellaneous:
SA_1 = SPST switch

9. Equalizers

Equalizers belong to the most versatile, but also most expensive filter circuits. They are used primarily to eradicate the discolouration of sound wherever this may happen in the chain of audio equipment. Although loudspeaker enclosures and room acoustics are the main culprits, the frequency response of microphones, pickups, cassette decks, and so on, also adversely affect the sound.

Basically, there are two types of equalizer: the graphic equalizer and the parametric equalizer.

Graphic equalizer

The most widely used equalizer is the graphic equalizer. Depending on its design, this type of equalizer may have between three and 31 shift controls whose setting determines the frequency response characteristic. Operating the equalizer is relatively simple: each control is associated with one specific frequency range. The more controls the equalizer has, the narrower the frequency ranges and the more versatile the control prospects.

Parametric equalizer

The operation of a parametric equalizer is quite different from that of a graphic equalizer. It does not only pre-emphasize or attenuate certain frequencies or narrow bands of frequencies, but also permits these to be shifted. Moreover, most parametric equalizers have a facility for varying the width of bands of frequencies. This means that for each range of frequencies three controls are required. Consequently, the number of frequency bands that can be accommodated is much smaller than with a graphic equalizer: only 1–3, depending on the design. Also, the operation of a parametric equzlier is rather more tedious than that of a graphic equalizer.

Which equalizer should be used?

The graphic equalizer is ideal for use when a number of resonances and other inequalizties over a fairly wide frequency band have to be equalized. The parametric equalizer is much better when a single frequency or narrow band of frequencies must be processed. For example, during live performances it enables feedback frequencies to be filtered out. Also, recorded music, especially that recorded during live performances, may be enhanced with the aid of a parametric equalizer. Even faint feedback whistles can be removed without affecting the remainder of the music. This is not possible with a graphic equalizer.

Graphic equalizer

Construction and operation

Almost all graphic equalizers are designed on the principle shown in Figure 9-1. The individual bandpass sections are used as forward filters (direction $R_1 \rightarrow R_2$) or reverse filters (through feedback in the direction $R_3 \rightarrow R_4$) under the control of potentiometers P_1-P_4 (there may be more than four, of course).

The theory of the filters has already been described in 'Filter in a feedback loop' (Chapter 7). The individual filter sections that are linked to the potentiometers function as a series resonant circuit to earth. One such section is shown in Figure 9-1b. A ten-band equalizer, for instance, contains ten such sections, whose component values are different, of course.

Figure 9-1. Basic design of a graphic equalizer (a) and of an individual filter section (b)

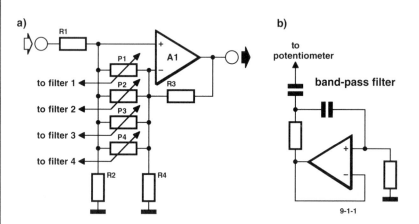

Values of filter components
A good graphic equalizer must, of course, meet certain requirement as far as frequency response is concerned. For instance, in Figure 9-2, the upper curve shows the frequency response of a 10-band equalizer in which all frequency bands are pre-emphasized. The two lower curves represent the frequency response when the frequency bands are pre-emphasized and attenuated alternately. Since the equal-

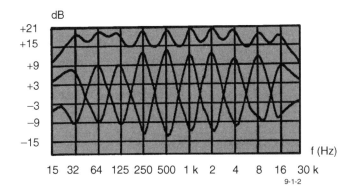

izer being considered is an octave type (one control per octave), the centre frequencies of the individual bands are more or less at right angles to the x-axis of the diagram. The calculation of the component values of such an equalizer is a tedious matter, because it normally results in non-standard values of the resistors and capacitors. The correct filter frequencies and bandwidths can be obtained only by combinations of certain values of resistors and capacitors. Moreover, the combination of components in each individual section must have different values from that in other sections. A further problem is that the resistor at the output of the operational amplifier in a filter determines not only the centre frequency and the bandwidth but also the depth of the filter and thus the control range. The three first sections in the equalizer used for Figure 9-2 (with centre frequencies 32 Hz, 64 Hz and 128 Hz), for instance, have larger value resistors than the other sections and the consequent smaller control range is clear in the frequency response curves.

It would be greatly advantageous if in the individual sections only the value of the capacitors had to be altered and the resistors all had the same value. This is possible if the problem is tackled in a different manner.

Changing capacitor values only

Although it is virtually impossible to obtain non-standard-value capacitors, it will be seen that the ratio of successive values in the standard range (0.001 μF, 0.0015 μF, 0.0022 μF, 0.0033 μF, 0.0047 μF, ...) is fairly constant at 1.47. If successive values of capacitor were used in successive filter sections, this ratio would result in a separation of centre frequencies of 0.554 octave. The ratio of every other value of capacitor is about 2.15 and this would result in a separation of centre frequencies of 1.11 octave. If thus the centre frequencies of the filter sections are chosen so that they are separated by one of these ratios, the calculation of the values of the filter

117

components becomes significantly easier.

This method is used in the design of the following equalizer circuits. Although therefore the individual control frequencies do not correspond to standard values, the bandwidths and frequency separations of the various sections are more constant. And, after all, what does it matter whether the control frequencies are separated by one octave or 1.1 octave?

Advantages of adding an operational amplifier

In the standard setup of an equalizer shown in Figure 9-1, the control of all frequency bands is assumed by a single operational amplifier, A_1. It is, however, better to use two op amps in cascade for this purpose, and this is done in the following control circuits. The individual filter sections are linked alternately to the first and second op amp. The resulting equalizer circuit, here an eight-band model, is shown in Figure

Figure 9-3.
Circuit diagram of an
8-band graphic
equalizer (a), and that
of each individual filter
section (b).

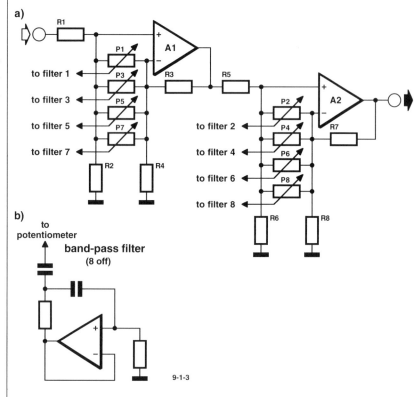

9-3.

The division of the control over two stages improves the frequency response. This is because the individual sections do not just present a frequency-dependent impedance to ground, but, like any RC network, they also cause a frequency-dependent phase shift. This (adverse) shift is particularly noticeable at the transition from a section to the next. Moreover, the effect is mutual, so that when the pre-emphasis of several adjacent sections is the same, it will affect adjacent frequency bands and this will be discernible by small irregularities in the frequency response.

If the control of adjacent frequency bands is split between two stages as shown in Figure 9-3, the mutual interaction of adjacent sections is largely obviated.

An added benefit of this method is the reduction in resistance at the inputs of the op amps. Compared with a single control op amp, the amplifiers in Figure 9-3 have only half as many potentiometers between their inverting and non-inverting inputs. True, owing to the feedback, the resistance between the inputs has no effect whatsoever. However, this assumes that the open-circuit voltage amplification (that is, without feedback) is theoretically infinitely high. In practice, this is not quite so, since at high frequencies the op amp quickly reaches its limits. This problem becomes even more problematic when, for example, one of the controls is set for high-frequency pre-emphasis. Such a resistive load between the inputs of the op amp lowers the open-circuit voltage gain, so that the actual amplification is finite and may easily be lowered. If this happens, the distortion increases. Dividing the control over two op amps reduces this problem.

Universal PCB for graphic equalizer

Construction of the following 4-band, 8-band, 12-band, and 16-band, graphic equalizer circuits is virtually identical. They differ only in the number of filter sections and in the component values. This means that they can be built on the same design of printed-circuit board. The filter sections all use quadruple op amps Type TL074. The 16-band model therefore needs only four ICs, the 12-band only three, the eight-band, two; and the four-band, only one. Populating the board is therefore very easy indeed.

A separate part of the circuit forms the actual control and also contains a variable preamplifier and impedance converter at the input. This part of the circuit is the same for all four versions and needs an additional quadruple op amp, also Type TL074.

Figure 9-4.
Circuit diagram for four
different graphic
equalizers: 4-band;
8-band; 12-band; and
16-band.

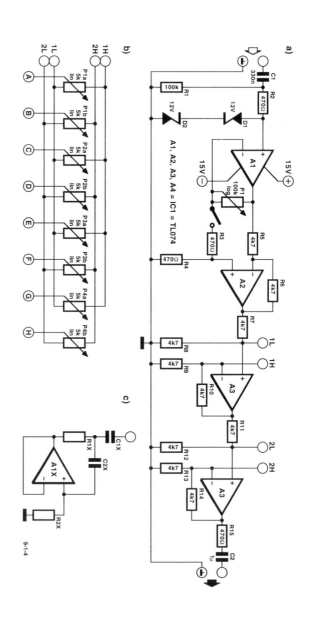

120

Components list for Figure 9-4 less filters

Resistors:

$R_1 = 100$ kΩ

$R_2, R_{15} = 470$ Ω

$R_3, R_4 = 470$ Ω, 1%

R_5–$R_{14} = 4.7$ kΩ, 1%

Capacitors:

$C_1 = 0.033$ μF

$C_2 = 1$ μF (not electrolytic)

Semiconductors:

D_1, D_2 = zener diode, 12 V, 500 mW

Integrated circuits:

IC_1 = TL074

Wiring the potentiometers

It is strongly recommended to use slide potentiometers for the operating controls, since, in contrast to rotary types, these show the setting of the frequency response at a glance. The potentiometers should be linked up with the shortest possible lengths of wire. The wire may be ordinary insulated circuit wire; screened wire is not necessary.

If the slide potentiometers are not screwed directly to the front panel, they need a separate board. It does not make sense to design a printed-circuit board for this, since, depending on the size and construction of the potentiometers, the pitch and position of the soldering pads on the PCB is indeterminate. It is, therefore, best to use straightforward prototyping board.

Another construction difficulty is the provision of the necessary slots for the slide potentiometers in the front panel. If you find this too tedious, use rotary controls, but, as already intimated, this makes reading the setting of the frequency response far more difficult.

Construction

The circuit diagram for the folllowing four graphic equalizers (four-band; eight-band; 12-band, and 16-band) is shown in Figure 9-4. The first two stages, A_1 and A_2, form a preamplifier whose amplification is variable between 0 and ×106. This amplifier is almost identical to the 'General purpose preamplifier' described in Chapter 6. The only differences between that and the present one lie in the values of a few components, and the addition of a switch in P_1. This switch enables the preamplifier to be switched on and off and also to set the amplification to unity. This is particularly advantageous when the circuit is duplicated to form a stereo unit, since loudness differences between the two channels are then avoided.

Stages A_3 and A_4 carry out the actual control of the single frequency bands. Potentiometers P_{1A}–P_{1H} are linked to terminals 1H, 1L, 2H and 2L as designated. The letter H (high) signifies the upper end of the slide potentiometer track, and L, the lower end, or, if rotary devices are used, H is fully anticlockwise, and L fully clockwise.

The eight frequency bands in Figure 9-4 are identified by the letters A–H; in the case of a 12-band equalizer, by the letters A–L, and in the case of a 16-band unit, by the letters A–P. The filters in the four-band version are identified by the letters A–D; in all cases, the letter A signifies the first frequency band.

Although Figure 9-4 shows the potentiometers for an eigfht-band equalizer only, the wiring up of the other versions follows identical lines, that is, the potentiometers are linked alternately to terminals 1H/1L and 2H/2L.

Figure 9-4c shows the circuit diagram of a single filter section, which is thus required four, eight, twelve, or sixteen times, depending on how many bands are wanted. The letter X represents the relevant filter identifying letter. The components in the filter with the lowest centre frequency, for instance, are designated R_{1A}, R_{2A}, C_{1A}, C_{2A} and A_{1A}.

Operation

After the input signal has passed through d.c. decoupling network R_1-C_1, and over-voltage protection circuit R_2-D_1-D_2, it is applied to op amp A_1. This amplifier operates as a non-inverting amplifier. The potential divider in the feedback loop consists of P_1, R_3, and R_4. The amplification may be varied from unity to $\times 107$.

The signal at the non-inverting input of A_1 is equal to the input signal to the overall circuit and is amplified by unity. The output of A_1 is applied to differential amplifier A_2, which amplifies the output of A_1 by -1. Thus, the output of A_2 may be varied from 0 to -106 times the input signal.

When the potentiometer is set to H (or, in case of a rotary control, fully anticlockwise), A_1 amplifies by 1. Since the switch is open, A_2 operates as an inverting amplifier with an amplification factor of -1.

The combination of the filters and stages A_3 and A_4 forms the actual equalizer. The filters act as series resonant circuits to earth and thus have a high impedance at most frequencies in the audio range. This impedance drops to only a few hundred ohms at or near the resonant frequency, however.

When the potentiometer for a certain band is at its lower position (1L) or, in case of a rotary control, fully clockwise, the combination of the filter and resistor R_7 functions as a potential divider and the resonant frequency is attenuated. When it is in its upper position (1H) or fully anticlockwise, as the case may be, the combination of filter and resistor R_{10} forms a potential divider in the feedback loop. The resonant frequency is then lifted. When the potentiometer is somewhere between these two extreme positions, both effects take place simultaneously; at its centre position, the frequency response is unaffected.

After op amp A_3 in conjunction with filters A, C, E and G has processed each second frequency band, op amp A_4 processes the remaining bands in association with filters B, D, F and H. Finally, the signal is applied to the output terminal via resistor R_{15} and capacxitor C_2, which determine the output impedance and decouple any residual direct voltage.

Optional modifications
If the variable preamplifier is not needed, the potentiometers and resistor R_4 should be replaced by wire bridges and resistor R_3 omitted.

If desired, a potentiometer without switch may be used; the switch should then be replaced by a wire bridge.

Simple four-band equalizer

A four-band equalizer is particularly suitable for use as a simple, quick-action tone control. It provides a much better and different tone adjustment than that offered by the conventional standard systems. Of course, compared with an eight-band or 16-band versions, its facilities are limited, but it is unequalled for fast and simple operation. In this type of equalizer it is possible to use rotary instead of slider potentiometers without detriment.

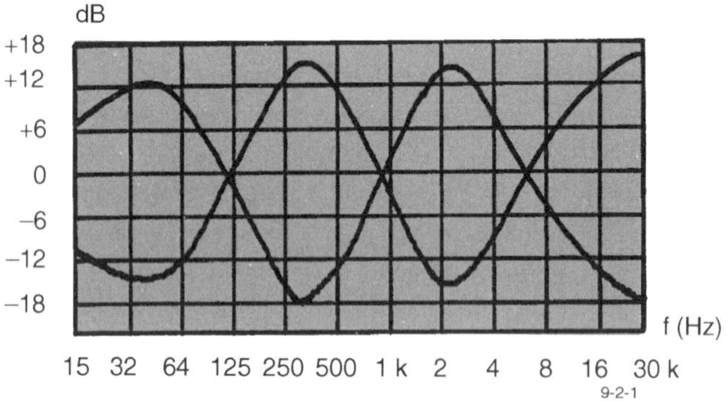

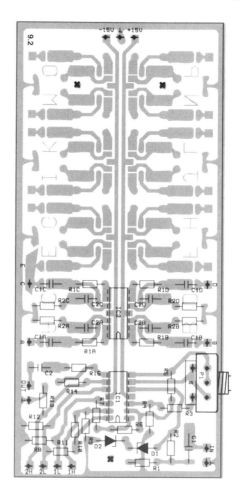

*Figure 9-5.
Frequency response of
the four-band graphic
equalizer.*

*Figure 9-6.
Component side of the
PC board for the
four-band equalizer;
the track side is given
in the Appendix.*

Filter data and components list

Filter No.	Centre frequency	Bandwidth in octaves	Components list (X represents the relevant filter identifying letter A–D				
			R_{1X}	R_{2X}	C_{1X}	C_{2X}	P_{1X}
A	50 Hz	2.74	330 Ω	100 kΩ	10 µF	33 nF	5 kΩ, lin
B	330 Hz	2.74	330 Ω	100 kΩ	1.5 µF	4.7 nF	5 kΩ, lin
C	2.3 kHz	2.74	330 Ω	100 kΩ	220 nF	680 pF	5 kΩ, lin
D	15 kHz	2.74	330 Ω	100 kΩ	33 nF	100 pF	5 kΩ, lin
			IC Type TL074				

The table contains the components for the four filters only. The components for the remainder of the circuit as well as the operation of the circuit are given on pages 121 and 116. If a stereo version is wanted, all circuits must be duplicated.

Note that capacitor C_{1A} may be formed from two parallel-connected 22 µF, 35 V electrolytic capacitors by interlinking their positive terminals. The negative terminals of the combination are soldered on to the PC board. It is good practice to solder a 1 MΩ resistor between the junction of the positive terminals and the 15 V supply rail (for instance, pin 4 of the TL074).

Eight-band equalizer

The eight-band equalizer is more than a simple tone control: it enables audio equipment to be adapted to the room acoustics and the frequency response of the loud-

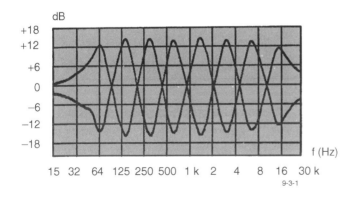

Figure 9-7.
The frequency response curves of the eight-band equalizer show the alternate lifting and cutting of the frequency bands.

speakers. In its simplest form, the eight-band equalizer may be compared with the commercial ten-octave equalizer, although its separation of the individual frequency bands is rather greater.

*Figure 9-8.
Component side of the
PC board for the
eight-band equalizer;
the track side is given
in the Appendix.*

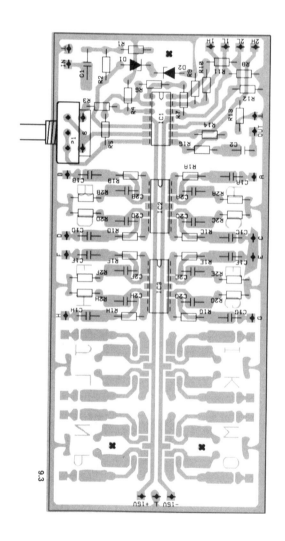

Filter data and components list

Filter No.	Centre frequency	Bandwidth in octaves	Components list (X represents the relevant filter identifying letter A–D				
			R_{1X}	R_{2X}	C_{1X}	C_{2X}	P_{1X}
A	65 Hz	1.11	330 Ω	82 kΩ	2.2 μF	100 nF	5 kΩ, lin
B	140 Hz	1.11	330 Ω	82 kΩ	1 μF	47 nF	5 kΩ, lin
C	300 Hz	1.11	330 Ω	82 kΩ	470 nF	22 pF	5 kΩ, lin
D	650 Hz	1.11	330 Ω	82 kΩ	220 nF	10 pF	5 kΩ, lin
E	1.4 kHz	1.11	330 Ω	82 kΩ	100 nF	47 nF	5 kΩ, lin
F	3 kHz	1.11	330 Ω	82 kΩ	47 nF	2.2 nF	5 kΩ, lin
G	6.5 kHz	1.11	330 Ω	82 kΩ	22 nF	1 nF	5 kΩ, lin
H	14 kHz	1.11	330 Ω	82 kΩ	10 nF	470 pF	5 kΩ, lin

2 off IC Type TL074

The table contains the components for the filters only. The components for the remainder of the circuit as well as the operation of the circuit are given on pages 121 and 116. If a stereo version is wanted, all circuits must be duplicated.

Sixteen-band equalizer

The sixteen-band equalizer offers a number of facilities for adapting the sound to the room acoustics and the frequency response of the loudspeakers. For optimum adaptation, start by setting the controls to their centre positions and listening to a

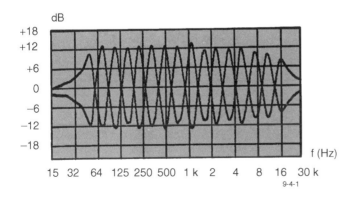

Figure 9-9.
Frequency response curves when the individual frequency bands are alternately lifted and cut.

9-4-1

127

variety of music before deciding on the final control settings.

Figure 9-10.
Component side of the
PC board for the six-
teen-band equalizer;
the track side is given in
the Appendix.

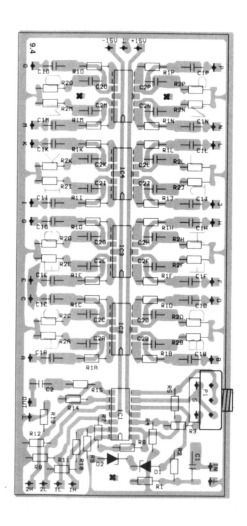

Filter data and components list

Filter No.	Centre frequency	Bandwidth in octaves	Components list (X represents the relevant filter identifying letter A–D)				
			R_{1X}	R_{2X}	C_{1X}	C_{2X}	P_{1X}
A	50 Hz	0.55	330 Ω	100 kΩ	1.5 μF	220 nF	5 kΩ, lin
B	75 Hz	0.55	330 Ω	100 kΩ	1 μF	150 nF	5 kΩ, lin
C	110 Hz	0.55	330 Ω	100 kΩ	680 nF	100 pF	5 kΩ, lin
D	160 Hz	0.55	330 Ω	100 kΩ	470 nF	68 pF	5 kΩ, lin
E	230 Hz	0.55	330 Ω	100 kΩ	330 nF	47 nF	5 kΩ, lin
F	340 Hz	0.55	330 Ω	100 kΩ	220 nF	33 nF	5 kΩ, lin
G	500 Hz	0.55	330 Ω	100 kΩ	150 nF	22 nF	5 kΩ, lin
H	750 Hz	0.55	330 Ω	100 kΩ	100 nF	15 nF	5 kΩ, lin
I	1.1 kHz	0.55	330 Ω	100 kΩ	68 nF	10 nF	5 kΩ, lin
J	1.6 kHz	0.55	330 Ω	100 kΩ	47 nF	6.8 nF	5 kΩ, lin
K	2.3 kHz	0.55	330 Ω	100 kΩ	33 nF	4.7 nF	5 kΩ, lin
L	3.4 kHz	0.55	330 Ω	100 kΩ	22 nF	3.3 nF`	5 kΩ, lin
M	5 kHz	0.55	330 Ω	100 kΩ	15 nF	2.2 nF	5 kΩ, lin
N	7.5 kHz	0.55	330 Ω	100 kΩ	10 nF	1.5 nF	5 kΩ, lin
O	11 kHz	0.55	330 Ω	100 kΩ	6.8 nF	1 nF	5 kΩ, lin
P	16 kHz	0.55	330 Ω	100 klZ	4.7 nF	680 pF	5 kΩ, lin

2 off IC Type TL074

The table contains the components for the filters only. The components for the remainder of the circuit as well as the operation of the circuit are given on pages 121 and 116. If a stereo version is wanted, all circuits must be duplicated.

Twelve-band equalizer for electric guitars

The twelve-band equalizer is intended specifically for use with electric guitars. The data of the individual filters are the same as those for the sixteen-band equalizer discussed in the previous section, but the frequecy bands around 50 Hz, 75 Hz, 110 Hz, and 16 kHz are not included. The remaining range from about 130 Hz to around 13 kHz is more than sufficient for electric guitars. In brief, the present equalizer provides the same control facilities as the sixteen-band model. It must therefore be borne in mind that the twelve-band equalizer is strictly for use with electric guitars; if other

Figure 9-11.
Component side of the
PC board for the
twelve-band equalizer
for electric guitars; the
track side is given in
the Appendix.

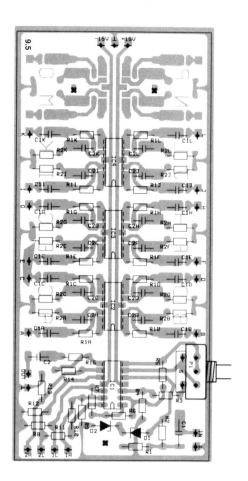

uses are also envisaged, the sixteen-band equalizer should be built.

Filter data and components list

Filter No.	Centre frequency	Bandwidth in octaves	Components list (X represents the relevant filter identifying letter A–D R_{1X}	R_{2X}	C_{1X}	C_{2X}	P_{1X}
A	160 Hz	0.55	330 Ω	82 kΩ	470 nF	68 nF	5 kΩ, lin
B	230 Hz	0.55	330 Ω	82 kΩ	330 nF	47 nF	5 kΩ, lin
C	340 Hz	0.55	330 Ω	82 kΩ	220 nF	33 pF	5 kΩ, lin
D	500 Hz	0.55	330 Ω	82 kΩ	150 nF	22 pF	5 kΩ, lin
E	750 Hz	0.55	330 Ω	82 kΩ	100 nF	15 nF	5 kΩ, lin
F	1.1 kHz	0.55	330 Ω	82 kΩ	68 nF	10 nF	5 kΩ, lin
G	1.6 kHz	0.55	330 Ω	82 kΩ	47 nF	6.8 nF	5 kΩ, lin
H	2.3 kHz	0.55	330 Ω	82 kΩ	33 nF	4.7 nF	5 kΩ, lin
I	3.4kHz	0.55	330 Ω	100 kΩ	22 nF	3.3 nF	5 kΩ, lin
J	5 kHz	0.55	330 Ω	100 kΩ	15 nF	2.2 nF	5 kΩ, lin
K	7.5 kHz	0.55	330 Ω	100 kΩ	10 nF	1.5 nF	5 kΩ, lin
L	11 kHz	0.55	330 Ω	100 kΩ	6.8 nF	1 nF	5 kΩ, lin

2 off IC Type TL074

The table contains the components for the filters only. The components for the remainder of the circuit as well as the operation of the circuit are given on pages 121 and 116 respectively.

Twelve-band equalizer for bass guitars

The equalizer described in this section is intended primarily for use with a bass guitar. As in the twelve-band model for electric guitars, the filter frequencies are identical to those in the sixteen-band equqzlier, but those for 5 kHz, 7.5 kHz, 11 kHz, and 16 kHz are not included. The variable frequency range stretches therefore from about 40 Hz to around 4 kHz, which is more than adequate for bass guitars and similar instruments. Here also, bear in mind that the present equalizer is for use with

Figure 9-12. Component side of the PC board for the twelve-band equalizer for bass guitars; the track side is given in the Appendix.

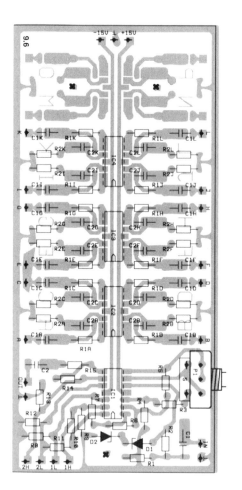

bass guitars and similar instruments only; if use with other types of equipment are foreseen, build the sixteen-band model.

Filter data and components list

Filter No.	Centre frequency	Bandwidth in octaves	Components list (X represents the relevant filter identifying letter A–D R_{1X}	R_{2X}	C_{1X}	C_{2X}	P_{1X}
A	50 Hz	0.55	330 Ω	82 kΩ	1.5 μF	220 nF	5 kΩ, lin
B	75 Hz	0.55	330 Ω	82 kΩ	1 μF	150 nF	5 kΩ, lin
C	110 Hz	0.55	330 Ω	82 kΩ	680 nF	100 pF	5 kΩ, lin
D	160 Hz	0.55	330 Ω	82 kΩ	470 nF	68 pF	5 kΩ, lin
E	230 Hz	0.55	330 Ω	82 kΩ	330 nF	47 nF	5 kΩ, lin
F	340 Hz	0.55	330 Ω	82 kΩ	220 nF	33 nF	5 kΩ, lin
G	500 Hz	0.55	330 Ω	82 kΩ	150 nF	22 nF	5 kΩ, lin
H	750 Hz	0.55	330 Ω	82 kΩ	100 nF	15 nF	5 kΩ, lin
I	1.1 kHz	0.55	330 Ω	100 kΩ	68 nF	10 nF	5 kΩ, lin
J	1.6 kHz	0.55	330 Ω	100 kΩ	47 nF	6.8 nF	5 kΩ, lin
K	2.3 kHz	0.55	330 Ω	100 kΩ	33 nF	4.7 nF	5 kΩ, lin
L	3.4 kHz	0.55	330 Ω	100 kΩ	22 nF	3.3 nF	5 kΩ, lin

2 off IC Type TL074

The table contains the components for the filters only. The components for the remainder of the circuit as well as the operation of the circuit are given on pages 121 and 116 respectively.

Calculation of graphic equalizers

If the properties mentioned in the foregoing sections do not meet your requirements, it is, of course, possible to design your own equalizer. The only problem with this is the value of the filter components, since the individual filter frequencies as well as the bandwidths must be recalculated.

Choosing the frequencies

Before anything else, the frequencies for each separate control must be determined. Start by choosing a value for the lowest-frequency section, say, 40 Hz. Next, choose a single factor between 1.4 and 4 to determine the frequency separation between controls. The other frequencies are easily calculated from these two values. If, for instance, the lowest frequency is 40 Hz and the separation factor is 2, the other frequencies are 80 Hz, 160 Hz, 320 Hz, 640 Hz, ...

If fewer frequency bands are needed, repeat the calculations with a larger factor; if more are required, with a smaller factor. It is, of course, also possible to lower the first frequency to a desired value. The factor depicting the frequency separation will be designated X in calculations of the bandwidth later on.

Calculating the filter data

Figure 9-13 shows once more the familiar circuit of a filter section used for every

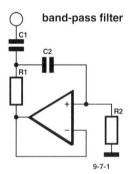

band-pass filter

9-7-1

frequency band. The equation

$$f = 1/2\pi RC$$

enables two frequencies to be calculated. The frequency determined by R_1 and C_1 is a certain factor higher than the actual filter frequency. The second frequency, determined by R_2 and C_2 is lower than the filter frequency by the same factor.

Example
If we assume that the frequency determined by R_1 and C_1 is 4 kHz, and that by R_2 and C_2 is 1 kHz, the filter frequency is $\sqrt{(1\times4)} = 2$ kHz. So, the factor by which the two frequencies differ from the filter frequency is 2. This factor determines the bandwidth of the filter and is depicted in the following by Y.

The closer together the individual frequencies of the equalizer are, the narrower the bandwidth of the individual sections has to be. This means that Y has to be chosen fairly large. Remember, however, that earlier we established a factor X for the distance between the frequency bands. Then,

$$Y = \log 13 / \log X.$$

In reality, the calculation is rather more complex, but this simple equation gives very acceptable values close to the actual ones.

Calculation of the filter components

We now know the value of the individual sections and factor Y, which is the same for all sections. The component values are then calculated as follows.

$$C_1 = 1/2\pi R_1 fY.$$

If giving R_1 a value of 330 Ω yields a non-standard value for C_1, make $R_1 = 390$ Ω.

$$C_2 = Y/2\pi R_2 f.$$

If giving R_2 a value of 100 kΩ results in a non-standard value for C_2, make $R_2 = 82$ kΩ.

The two equations enable all components for all the sections to be calculated; do not forget to alter the value of the frequency in the calculations, which is easily done. Note that factor Y remains the same throughout.

If you want to check the filter data with the component values, use the following equations.

$$f = 1/2\pi \sqrt{(R_1 R_2 C_1 C_2)}$$

$$Y = \sqrt{(R_2 C_2 / R_1 C_1)}$$

Parametric equalizers

A parametric equalizer allows only one frequency band to be processed. In contrast to a graphic equalizer, however, it permits the variation of several parameters. Both the frequency and the bandwidth may be set with the aid of two potentiometers. The third potentiometer is, as in a graphic equalizer, required for lifting or cut-

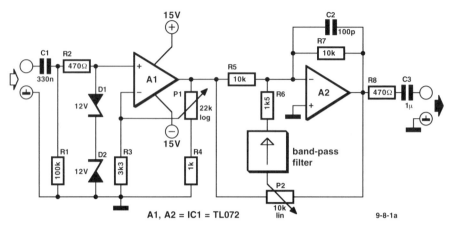

Figure 9-14.
Diagram of the
main circuit of the
parametric
equalizer.

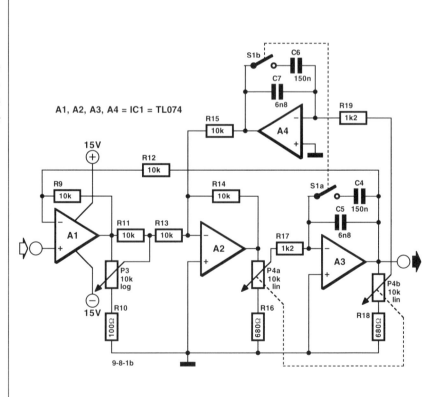

Figure 9-15.
Circuit diagram of the
bandpass filter con-
tained in the
parametric
equalizer.

ting the response. A further potentiometer enables the input signal to be amplified by a factor of 1–32 (that is, 0–30 dB), which enables weak inputs to be used directly.

To ensure that the control covers the whole audio band, two frequency ranges are needed. Therefore, apart from the frequency-setting potentiometer, there is a switch to change between two frequency ranges. In the lower range, the frequency may be set from 35 Hz up to 840 Hz, and in the upper range, between 810 Hz and 19.5 kHz.

Circuit description

For clarity's sake, the circuit diagram has been split into two: Figure 9-14 shows the actual main circuit of the equalizer. The variable bandpass filter (between P_2 and R_6) is shown as a simple square, in which the arrow indicates the direction of the signal. The circuit of the filter is given in Figure 9-15.

In figure 9-14, stage A_1 functions as an impedance converter. However, the variable potential divider in the feedback loop enables the signal to be amplified by a factor of up to 32, which means that very weak signals can also be processed. When P_1 is set fully anticlockwise, A_1 functions purely as an impedance converter, that is, without any amplification.

The second stage, op amp A_2, in conjunction with the bandpass filter, forms the equalizer proper. We will assume that the bandpass filter has a resonance frequency of 1 kHz and that P_2 is set fully clockwise (which means that the wiper is linked directly to the junction of R_5 and P_1). In this situation, a 1 kHz signal is applied to the inverting input of A_2 not just via R_5, but also via the bandpass filter and R_6. The consequent additional signal current through R_6 increases the amplification of A_2.

When P_2 is set fully anticlockwise, however, that is, when its wiper is linked directly to the junction of R_7 and R_8, resistor R_6 is effectively in parallel with R_7. When a signal outside the range of the resonant frequency is applied, there is, of course, no output (or only a tiny one) from the bandpass filter. There is no current through R_6, and the amplification of A_2 is then determined by R_5 and R_7. Since these resistors have the same value, the amplification of A_2 is unity. Note that capacitor C_2 has no discernible effect on the amplification; it serves merely to suppress any oscillations in the ultrasonic range.

The maximum lift or cut of the response can be calculated from the values of R_5, R_6, and R_7; with values as specified, it is ± 17.7 dB. In reality, the equalizer has a control range of ± 20 dB. The difference arises from the fact that the type of bandpass used does not just pass the resonance frequency, but lifts it by about 6 dB.

The circuit of the bandpass filter in Figure 9-16 is very similar to that in Figure 7-14. However, the present filter uses the non-inverting and not the inverting input

Figure 9-16.
(a) Frequency response with different quality settings.

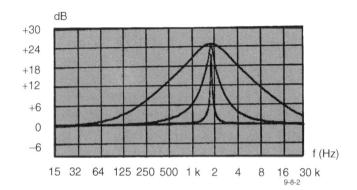

(b) Frequency response with different degrees of lift and cut.

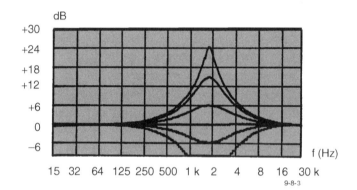

(c) Frequency response with the lowest and highest frequencies lifted.

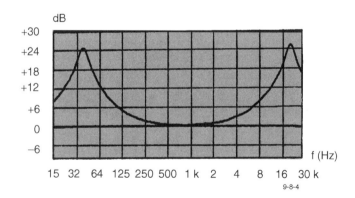

of the first op amp. This results in the 6 dB gain mentioned in the previous paragraph.

Some readers may find the arrangement of quality control P_3 and frequency control P_4 unusual, since the resistors to earth (R_{10}, R_{16}, R_{18}) seem superfluous. However, these resistors enable the control ranges to be spread nearly uniformly over the angle of rotation of the potentiometers. The frequency controls should really consist of a logarithmic stereo potentiometer. Unfortunately, this kind of device gives a far from uniform control, certainly very inferior to that of linear potentiometers, and would therefore cause the Q(uality) to vary with frequency variations. The arrangement as shown gives the overall control a logarithmic characteristic although linear potentiometers are used.

Apart from the resistors, capacitors C_5 and C_7 also affect the frequency, of course. When these components have a value of 0.0068 μF, the filter frequency can be varied from 810 Hz up to 19.5 kHz. When switch S_1 is closed, capacitors C_4 and C_6 are in parallel with C_5 and C_7 respectively. The control range then extends from 35 Hz up to 840 Hz.

Optional modifications

If the variable preamplifier is not needed, input stage A_1 may be used simply as an impedance converter. In that case, potentiometer P_1 and resistors R_3 and R_4 may be omitted. Also, the inverting input of A_1 must be strapped to the output of the op amp.

Components list

Resistors:
R_1 = 100 kΩ
R_2, R_8 = 470 Ω
R_3 = 3.3 kΩ, 1%
R_4 = 1 kΩ, 1%
R_5, R_7, R_9, R_{11}–R_{15} = 10 kΩ, 1%
R_6 = 1.5 kΩ, 1%
R_{10} = 100 Ω, 1%
R_{16}, R_{18} = 680 Ω, 1%
R_{17}, R_{19} = 1.2 kΩ, 1%
P_1 = 22 kΩ, log potentiometer
P_2 = 10 kΩ, linear potentiometer
P_3 = 10 kΩ, log potentiometer
P_4 = 2 off 10 kΩ linear potentiometer (see text)

Figure 9-17.
Component layout of
the printed-cicuit
board for the
parametric
equalizer. The track
layout is given in the
Appendix.

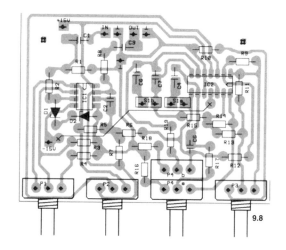

Capacitors:
$C_1 = 0.33 \, \mu F$
$C_2 = 100 \, pF$
$C_3 = 1 \, \mu F$ (not electrolyic)
$C_4, C_6 = 0.15 \, \mu F$, 5%
$C_5, C_7 = 0.0068 \, \mu F$, 5%

Semiconductors:
D_1, D_2 = zener diode. 12 V, 500 mA

Integrated circuits:
IC_1 = TL072
IC_2 = TL074

Miscellaneous:
S_1 = 2-pole single-throw switch

Three-fold parametric equalizer

The circuit in Figure 9-18 provides three variable parametric frequency bands.
Apart from lift and cut, the circuit also enables the frequency and bandwidth of
each band to be varied. Therefore, nine potentiometers (three per band) are
needed. As in the circuit in Figure 9-14, an additional potentiometer makes it

140

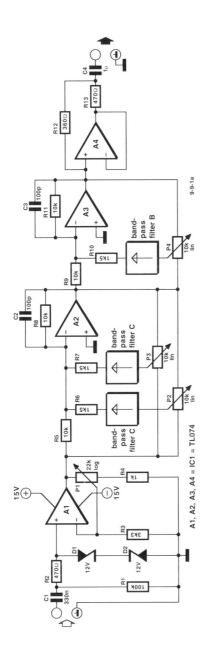

Figure 9-18.
Circuit diagram of the
3-fold parametric
equalizer.

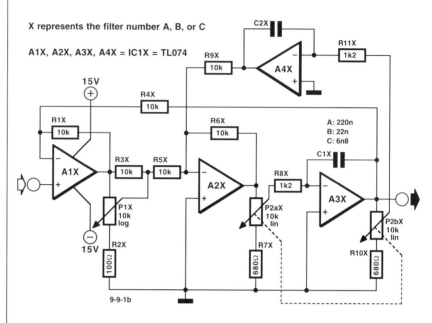

Figure 9-19.
Circuit diagram of one
of the bandpass filters
contained in the three-
fold parametric
equalizer.

possible to obtain a preamplification of the input signal of up to 30 dB. Each of the three frequency bands covers a part of the audio range; a range switch as in Figure 9-14 is, therefore, not needed. The lowest band covers 25 Hz to 600 Hz, the centre band, 250 Hz to 6 kHz, and the upper band, 810 Hz to 19 kHz.

Circuit description

Since the construction and operation of the present equalizer are almost identical to those of the equalizer in Figure 9-14, only the differences between them will be discussed.

In Figure 9-18, the three frequency bands are controlled by op amps A_2 and A_3. The filters proper, A, B, and C, are shown as simple boxes. The lowest frequency band is covered by A, the centre by B, and the upper by C. In contrast to the equalizer in Figure 9-14, the filters in the present circuits can be varied over a limited frequency range only.

Op amp A_2 controls filters A and C, while filter B is controlled by op amp A_3. It would, in principle, be possible to control all three ranges by one op amp, but the filters would then interact with each other. This is so, because when the frequencies are close together, phase shifts that occur would cause variations in the frequency response. Since A_2 processes only the lowest and upper frequency bands, the separation between these bands ensures that any interaction is prevented.

The final stage in the circuit, A_4, is an impedance converter which ensures that the output signals of A_3 and itself are identical. Both these signals are used as output signal (via R_{12} and R_{13}), which enables a higher output current to be obtained.

The circuit of the three bandpass filters is shown in Figure 9-19. Its construction and operation are as described for the single parametric equalizer (Figure 9-14), but the frequency range switch is not used. The letter X represents filters A, B or C, as the case may be. Accordingly, the components for the centre-frequency filter (B) are designated A_{1B}, R_{1B}, R_{2B}, and so on. The components for the three filters are identical, with the exception of capacitors C_{1X} and C_{2X}.

Components list
Resistors:
$R_1 = 100$ kΩ
R_{1A}, R_{3A}–R_{6A}, R_{9A}, R_{1B}, R_{3B}–R_{6B}, R_{9B}, R_{1C}, R_{3C}–R_{6C}, $R_{9C} = 10$ kΩ, 1%
R_2, $R_{13} = 470$ Ω
R_{2A}, R_{2B}, $R_{2C} = 100$ Ω, 1%
$R_3 = 3.3$ kΩ, 1%
$R_4 = 1$ kΩ, 1%
R_5, R_8, R_9, $R_{11} = 10$ kΩ, 1%
R_6, R_7, $R_{10} = 1.5$ kΩ, 1%
R_{7A}, R_{10A}, R_{7B}, R_{10B}, R_{7C}, $R_{10C} = 680$ Ω, 1%
R_{8A}, R_{11A},R_{8B}, R_{11B},R_{7C}, $R_{11C} = 1.2$ kΩ, 1%
$R_{12} = 560$ Ω
$P_1 = 22$ kΩ, log potentiometer
P_{1A}, P_{1B}, $P_{1C} = 10$ kΩ, log potentiometer
P_2, P_3, $P_4 = 10$ kΩ, linear potentiometer
P_{2A}, P_{2B}, $P_{2C} = 2$ off 10 kΩ, linear potentiometer (see text)

Capacitors:
$C_1 = 0.33$ μF
C_2, $C_3 = 100$ pF
$C_4 = 1$ μF (not electrolytic)
C_{1A}, $C_{2A} = 0.22$ μF, 5%
C_{1B}, $C_{2B} = 0.022$ μF, 5%

Figure 9-20. Component layout of the printed- circuit board for the three-fold parametric equalizer. The track layout is given in the Appendix.

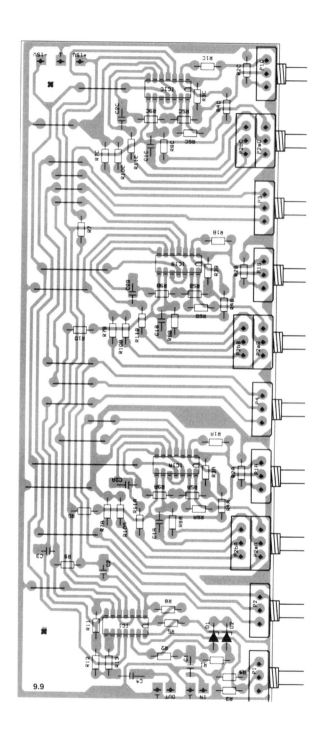

C_{1C}, C_{2C} = 0.0068 μF, 5%

Semiconductors:
D_1, D_2 = zener diode, 12 V, 500 mA

Integrated circuits:
IC_1, IC_{1A}, IC_{1B}, IC_{1C} = TL074

Optional modifications
With the values of C_{1X} and C_{2X} as specified below, frequency ranges are obtained as follows:
Filter A:
   25 Hz to 600 Hz (C_{1A}, C_{2A} = 0.22 μF)
Filter B:
   250 Hz to 6 kHz (C_{1A}, C_{2A} = 0.022 μF)
Filter C:
   810 Hz to 19 kHz (C_{1A}, C_{2A} = 0.0068 μF)
If different frequency ranges are desired, the values of the capacitors may, of course, be changed accordingly. Values for some suggested frequency bands are given below. Note that in each filter the two capacitors must have the same value. If the variable preamplifier is not needed, the modifications given for the single parametric equalizer (Figure 9-14) may be incorporated.

Frequency range	Value of C_{1X} and C_{2X}
17 Hz to 420 Hz	0.33 μF
25 Hz to 600 Hz	0.22 μF
37 Hz to 880 Hz	0.15 μF
55 Hz to 1.5 kHz	0.1 μF
81 Hz to 1.9 kHz	0.068 μF
120 Hz to 2.8 kHz	0.047 μF
170 Hz to 4.2 kHz	0.033 μF
250 Hz to 6 kHz	0.022 μF
370 Hz to 6.8 kHz	0.015 μF
550 Hz to 13 kHz	0.01 μF
810 Hz to 19 kHz	0.0068 μF
1.2 kHz to 28 kHz	0.0047 μF

Operating hints for parametric equalizers

Parametric equalizers such as described in this chapter are used primarily for the suppression of an interfering frequency (band). A multi-fold parametric equalizer is particularly useful during the setting up of a live music performance, where interference resonances arise owing to the different frequency responses of microphones, pick-ups and PA loudspeakers, not to speak of the acoustics of many rooms and halls. Many control panels are therefore provided with a parametric equalizer for each channel.

Attenuation of interference resonances

Usually, the interference resonance occupies only a narrow band of frequencies, often less than an octave wide. To detect the resonance, start with the bandwidth control of the equalizer set fully anticlockwise (narrow bandwidth, high Q). Next, lift the frequency response with the dB control, possibly up to maximum lift, but be careful with public-adress equipment. In this, too much lift can give rise to unpleasant positive feedback. It may be necessary to lower the volume control of the equipment. When in this condition the frequency control is adjusted, the interference resonance is normally easily found. When the set frequency is identical to the resonance, the latter is amplified, which sounds even more unpleasant.

When the frequency is set correctly, turn the dB control anticlockwise (cut). If the resonance is not completely suppressed, broaden the bandwidth slightly (bandwidth control clockwise). Finally, turn the dB control anticlockwise until the resonance is no longer noticeable.

Parametric equalizer in the hi-fi installation

The parametric equalizer may be used to good effect in a domestic hi-fi installation to equalize the frequency response of the loudspeakers and the room acoustics. In a stereo setup, two equalizers are needed, of course. The instructions for adjusting the three controls are similar to those given earlier for the three-fold parametric equalizer. It is, however, better to set up the two channels independently of one another and this is done per channel while the other channel is switched off with the balance control.

It is, of course, true that the sound quality of an hi-fi installation is determined not only by the room acoustics and the frequency response of the loudspeakers, but also by the characteristic sound of the recording or broadcast programme being played. However, it does not make sense to spend a couple of minutes to set up the equalizer every time another recording or radio programme is listened to. In practice, a compromise must be sought of the controls settings for a number of different recordings. To this end, listen to, say, four or five different recordings of, for instance, a piano, a violin, a clarinet, and so on, and find settings that are pleasing to all four or five. This will take a little time, but the end result is well worth it.

Post production of live performances

Orchestras and bands are often faced with the difficulty of producing usable recordings of their music, for example, demonstation cassettes. To do so in a studio is expensive, and test recordings with an 8-track tape recorder do not always give the best results either. Although a simple recording during a live performance is not necessarily any better, it is certainly less expensie and requires less time and effort. Fortunately, the quality of such recordings can often be enhanced siginificantly afterwards. Of course, serious flaws cannot be remedied, but annoying resonances can normally be reduced appreciably. The setting up of the equalizer(s) is as decribed earlier; it is, of course, essential that the sound of the loudspeakers used is not affected. Just as during the setting up of the equalizer(s) the sound of the music being played should not be included, so in this case, the response of the loudspeakers and the room acoustics should not be taken into account. Therefore, the setting up should preferably be carried out with the use of good-quality loudspeakers (a pair of hi-fi headphones may also be used). It is very useful to make a direct comparison of the sound with that of a different piece of music (from a CD).

When the optimum setting of the controls has been established, simply copy the enhanced version on to a new cassette, but preferably on a reel-to-reel tape recorder. Even a hi-fi stereo video recorder is better than a cassette recorder. If it concerns a stereo recording, the equalizer should, of course, also be a stereo version. If a high-quality mono(phonic) video recorder is available, it is possible to enhance one channel at a time. When one channel has been processed, copy it on to a good-quality tape. Play this back and at the same time process the other channel; the resulting two-channel recording is then re-recorded on a new tape.

Filtering out feedback

One of the more interesting aspects of a parametric equalizer is the possibility of eliminating feedback whistles on existing recordings, such as those produced in parallel with a live performance. This is done by setting the Q-control fully anticlockwise (minimum bandwidth, maximum Q), followed by setting the dB-control fully clockwise. Next, play back the recording and adjust the frequency control to the frequency of the feedback. Owing to the narrow bandwidth, this setting must be exact so that the feedback whistle becomes even more audible. Then, turn the dB-control anticlockwise until the whistle disappears.

Unfortunately, not every feedback sound is eliminated so simply. For example, it may only be possible to attenuate strong feedback consisting of more than a single frequency (harmonics). Less strong feedback frequencies can, however, virtually always be eliminated entirely without any effect on the overall wanted sound.

10. Dynamic controls

Dynamic control involves the varying of the original volume-level. For instance, a limiter reduces the signal level at high volume settings to a level at which overdriving of the power stages is prevented. A noise gate, on the other hand, reduces the signal level at low volume settings and so suppresses background noise. There are also dynamic compressors and and expanders that reduce or enlarge the differences in sound level over the entire audio range. Noise suppression systems like Dolby or DBX operate on that principle. With these systems, the signal is compressed during the recording . When it is played back, a dynamic expander restores the original differences in sound level and so reduces the background noise.

Limiter

A limiter is of use only when the sound level must not exceed a predefined maximum value. It allows a public-address amplifier to be driven at high levels without the amplifier stages being overdriven. The same applies to cassette recordings in which a high recording drive results in a larger signal-to-noise ratio.

The circuit preceding the limiter provides a peak output voltage of about 2.5 W_{pp}. As soon as this level is exceeded, the limiter is enabled and restricts the signal to 2.5 W_{pp}. If a higher or lower output voltage is needed, a level matching circuit (see Figure 6-10) may be added to the output stage. All other parameters can be controlled with three potentiometers.

Control P_1 adjusts the input signal level and should be set to a position where the peak LED just does not light, even at larger input levels.

Control P_2 set the maximum amplification. It determines by what amount the amplification, and with it the signal-to-noise, increases when the limiter is disabled.

Control P_3 sets the time delay between an increase in signal level and the resulting actuation of the limiter.

Circuit description

In the circuit diagram in Figure 10-1, the input signal is applied via impedance converter A_1 and gain control P_1 to analogue multiplier IC_3. This device is like an op amp in that it has an inverting and a non-inverting input. The amplification cannot become infinite, however, but is determined by a control current that flows to the device via P_2. Therefore, unlike the op amp, the IC cannot use negative feedback. The output of the multiplier is terminated into resistor R_6, which is necessary since the device provides its output signal as a current. Without a terminating (load) resistance, a infinitely high output voltage would be required.

Network R_7-C_2 is a low-pass filter that removes any residual direct voltage.

Capacitor C_4 is a bypass for ultra-sonic frequencies and also suppresses any tendency of the stage to oscillate.

Op amp A_2 functions as a common impedance converter. Its output signal is applied to the output terminal of the limiter via C_5 and R_{16}. At the same time, this signal is also applied to the next stage, A_3, via D_5 and D_6. Here, potential dividers R_{10}-R_{13} and R_{11}-R_{12} provide a voltage of about +500 mV to the non-inverting input and one of about −500 mV to the inverting input. Op amp A_3 provides the maximum possible output of some 15 V.

When the output voltage of A_2 exceeds 1.2 V or drops below −1.2 V, op amp A_3 has a higher voltage at its inverting input than at its non-inverting input. The output of A_3 then changes the minimum level of −15 V. In this condition, capacitor C_6 is discharged rapidly via diode D_9. When the sound level drops, so that the output of A_3 becomes positive again, C_6 is charged via R_{14} and P_3. The charging rate depends on the setting of preset P_3.

The following stage, op amp A_4, is also an impedance converter, whose output controls the amplification of A_3 via R15, D_8 and P_2. The lower the potential across C_6, and thus also the output of A_4, the smaller the amplification of A_3. When the limiter is enabled, the potential at the output of A_4 is small, transistor T_1 is cut off, and D_{12} lights. If, however, A_4 provides the maximum output of some 15 V, T_1 is switched on via D_{10}, D_{11} and R_{17}, so that D_{12} is short-circuited.

The peak indicator, D_7, is driven by op amps A_5 and A_6. These amplifiers are connected in parallel to provide a higher output current. The non-inverting inputs of the op amps are provided with a constant voltage of 30 mV by potential divider R_4-R_5. When the input voltage of IC_3 exceeds this level, the op amps switch on the peak indicator via D_3, D_4, R_8 and R_9. The potential across capacitor C_3 holds the voltage across the LED at a more or less stable level so that

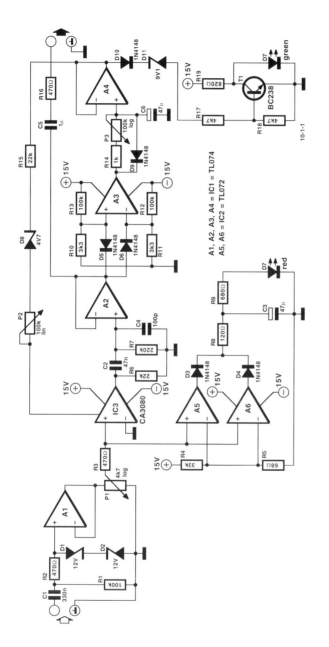

Figure 10-1.
Circuit diagram of the limiter.

151

Figure 10-2.
Component layout of
the printed-circuit
board for the limiter.
The track side is given
in the Appendix.

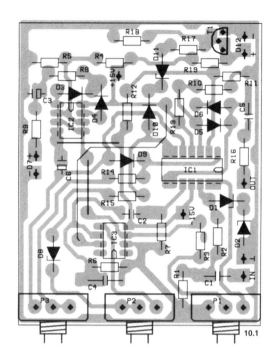

10.1

the diode does not flicker at every half period.

Components list

Resistors:

$R_1, R_{12}, R_{13} = 100 \text{ k}\Omega$

$R_2, R_3, R_{16} = 470 \, \Omega$

$R_4 = 33 \text{ k}\Omega$

$R_5 = 68 \, \Omega$

$R_6, R_{15} = 22 \text{ k}\Omega$

$R_7 = 220 \text{ k}\Omega$

$R_8 = 120 \, \Omega$

$R_9 = 680 \, \Omega$

$R_{10}, R_{11} = 3.3 \text{ k}\Omega$

$R_{14} = 1 \text{ k}\Omega$

$R_{17}, R_{18} = 4.7 \text{ k}\Omega$

$R_{19} = 820 \, \Omega$

$P_1 = 4.7 \text{ k}\Omega$, log

152

$P_2 = 100\ k\Omega$, linear
$P_3 = 100\ k\Omega$, log

Capacitors:
$C_1 = 0.33\ \mu F$
$C_2 = 0.047\ \mu F$
$C_3 = 47\ \mu F$, 16 V, radial
$C_4 = 100\ pF$
$C_5 = 1\ \mu F$ (not electrolytic)
$C_6 = 47\ \mu F$, 35 V, radial

Semiconductors:
D_1, D_2 = zener diode, 12 V, 500 mW
D_3–D_6, D_9, D_{10} = 1N4148
D_7 = LED, red
D_8 = zener diode 4.7 V, 500 mW
D_{11} = zener diode, 9.1 V, 500 mW
D_{12} = LED, green

Integrated circuits:
IC_1 = TL074
IC_2 = TL072
IC_3 = CA3080

Operation

Set the three potentiometers fully anticlockwise. Next, turn gain control P_1 until the red LED just does not light, even with high sound levels. The green LED should not light either. The maximum amplification for soft passages can be set with P_2. The green LED lights when limiting commences. The speed at which the amplification is restored after a limiting action is set with P_3: the more this control is turned clockwise, the lower the speed.

Optional modifications

The output voltage of 2.5 V_{pp} is too high for many applications. When a lower level is required, the value of resistors R_{10} and R_{11} may be reduced from 3.3 kΩ to 1 kΩ. This change lowers the output level to about 1.7 V_{pp}.

Dynamic compressor

The compressor reduces the dynamic range of audio signals in the same way as a limiter. It does not provide a fixed upper limit for the sound level, however, but it does reduce the dynamic range of the audio signal evenly.

The circuit is best suited for use with a cassette recorder which provides only a limited dynamic range. Compact disks normally have a dynamic range that cannot be used in cassette recordings: soft passages almost disappear below the noise floor. The same applies to microphone recordings when the sound level is subject to large variations. Here also, the differences in sound level are reduced to an acceptable magnitude.

The volume compressor is particularly useful with cassette recordings that are played back in a car because there soft passages are easily drowned out by the engine noise.

Circuit description

The circuit diagram of the dynamic compressor is shown in Figure 10-4. The dynamically-variable gain is provided by a special compander circuit, IC_2. The word compander is a contraction of compressor-expander: a noise reduction device which compresses the dynamic range prior to recording and expands the dynamic range by a complementary amount in playback. The type used here contains two companders for stereo applications. Companders normally operate as dynamic expanders, but when they are placed in the feedback loop

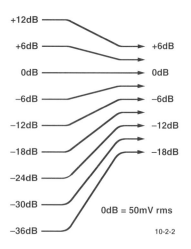

Figure 10-3. The relationship between input voltage and output voltage in graphic form.

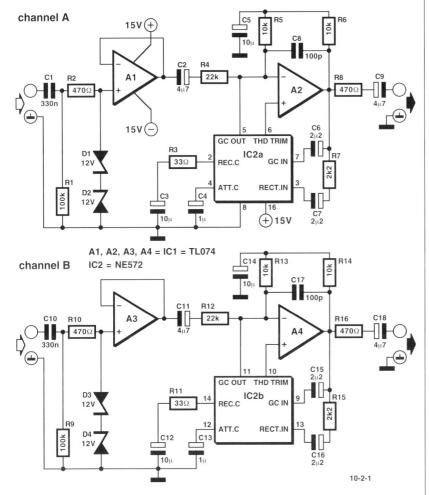

Figure 10-4.
Circuit diagram of the
dynamic compressor.

channel A

A1, A2, A3, A4 = IC1 = TL074
IC2 = NE572

channel B

10-2-1

as here (A$_2$ and A$_4$), they operate as compressors.

Operational amplifier A$_1$ functions as an impedance converter whose output is applied to the inverting input of A$_2$ via C$_2$ and R$_4$. Direct-voltage feedback is provided by R$_5$ and R$_6$. Since the audio signal consists of alternating voltages, it is partially fed back via C$_6$ and pin 7 and pin 5 of IC$_{2a}$.

The control input to IC$_{2a}$ is via pin 3. The voltage at this pin is rectified and smoothed by C$_3$ and C$_4$ before it is used to control the amplification. The exact relationship between the output voltage and input voltage is shown in Figure

155

10-3.

Capacitor C_8 provides high-frequency feedback to prevent any oscillations in the ultrasonic range.

The other channel, based on A_3, A_4 and IC_{2b} is, of course, identical to the one just discussed.

Optional modifications

When the level of the input signal drops, the compressor increases the amplification within seconds. In some cases, this may be undesirable, for instance, in speech passages when after each word the amplification, and thus the noise, would increase. This problem is easily remedied by slowing down the control action, which is effected by enlarging the values of C_3 and C_{12}: these may go up to as much as 1000 μF.

When the level of the input signal is very high, it may happen that the compressor is overdriven and crackles. This problem is overcome by increasing the value of R_4 and R_{12} to 47 kΩ.

Figure 10-5. Component layout of the printed-circuit board for the compressor. The track side is given in the Appendix.

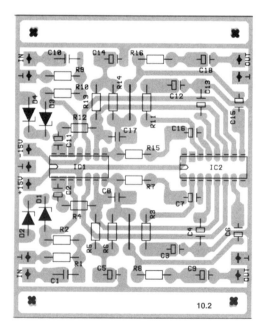

Components list

Resistors:

R_1, R_9 = 100 kΩ

R_2, R_8, R_{10}, R_{16} = 470 Ω

R_3, R_{11} = 33 Ω

R_4, R_{12} = 22 kΩ, 1%

R_5, R_6, R_{13}, R_{14} = 10 kΩ

R_7, R_{15} = 2.2 kΩ, 1%

Capacitors:

C_1, C_{10} = 0.33 μF

C_2, C_9, C_{11}, C_{18} = 4.7 μF, 16 V, radial

C_3, C_5, C_{12}, C_{14} = 10 μF, 16 V, radial

C_4, C_{13} = 1 μF, 16 V, radial

C_6, C_7, C_{15}, C_{16} = 2.2 μF, 16 V, radial

C_8, C_{17} = 100 pF

Semiconductors:

D_1–D_4 = zener diode, 12 V, 500 mW

Integrated circuits:

IC_1 = TL074

IC_2 = NE572

Noise gate

A noise gate is basically a signal-level-dependent switch. When the signal level exceeds a certain value, th signal is switched off completely. This ensures that interference noise and hum are suppressed effectively. The noise gate is particularly useful with electric guitars and electric percussion.

The input of a noise gate is normally high-impedance, so that an electric guitar can be connected to it without any problems. The level at which the gate opens can be predetermined with a preset. The present noise gate has a pre-amplifier for very weak signals whose amplification may be varied between unity and ×22.

The state of the gate is indicated at all times by three LEDs. The yellow one lights when a suitable signal is applied and the gate is open. The green and

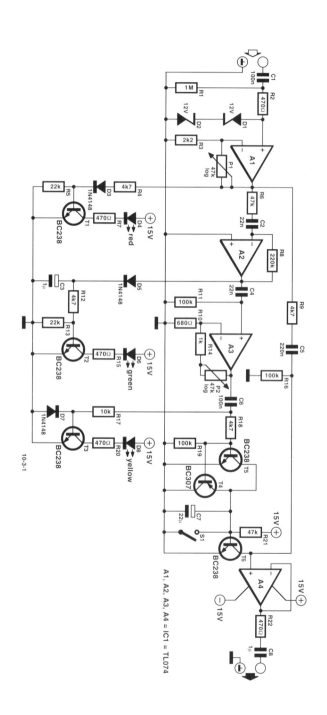

Figure 10-6.
Circuit diagram of the
noise gate.

A1, A2, A3, A4 = IC1 = TL074

10-3-1

158

red LEDs are level indicators to facilitate the setting of the gain controls. The green LED may flicker in rhythm with the signal. The red LED should remain off even when loud audio passages are input. The gate function may be disabled with a switch, whereupon the circuit functions as impedance converter or pre-amplifier.

Circuit description

The circuit diagram of the noise gate is shown in Figure 10-6. Up to the first stage, op amp A_1, the circuit is that of a standard preamplifier similar to several others in this book. An unusual aspect, however, is the relatively high input resistance (R_1) of 1 MΩ. This enables high-impedance sound sources, such as an electric guitar, to be coupled directly to the gate.

The output of A_1 is split into three branches. One drives the (red) peak indicator via R_4, D_3, T_1 and R_7. Transistor T_1 comes on as soon as the level of the input signal exceedss 1.5 V.

The other parts of the signal are applied to output stage A_4 via R_9 and C_5, and to op amp A_2 via R_6 and C_2. The latter stage amplifies the signal ×4.7and drives the green indicator, D_6, via D_5, R_{12}, T_2 and R_{15}. This indicator lights as soon as the level of the amplified signal exceeds 1.5 V.

Op amp A_3 amplifies the signal by a factor between ×2.5 and ×70 depending on the setting of P_2. When the output of A_3 has a negative level greater than –0.7 V, capacitor C_7 is short-circuited and discharged via T_4. When the output level of A_3 is more positive than –0.7 V, capacitor C_7 is discharged via T_5. At the same time, T_3 also conducts and causes the yellow indicator to light.

When the signal level exceeds the set threshold, transistors T_3, T_4 and T_5 are cut off and C_7 is charged rapidly via R_{21}. The potential across C_7 reaches a value of 0.7 V in a split second. Transistor T_6 then comes on and short-circuits the signal arriving via R_9 and C_5.

When the signal has an appropriate level again, C_7 is discharged rapidly via T_4 and T_5; T_6 is cut off and the signal is once more applied to the output terminal via A_4, R_{22} and C_8. The same action takes place when switch S_1 is closed: C_7 is discharged and T_6 is cut off.

High-pass sections R_6-C_2 and R_{11}-C_4 prevent the gate being operated by hum and noise alone.

The lower section of the diagram containing the indicator diodes and their drivers has separate power inputs for 0 V (ground) and +15 V. The power lines should be kept separate up to the power supply to prevent any clicking and crackling in the output caused by LED action.

Optional modifications

If the noise gate is used primarily with bass instruments, the value of capacitors C_2 and C_4 should be 0.047 μF to ensure that the gate opens without any problems at very low frequencies. However, if the gate is used primarily for the elimination of low hum, the value of these capacitors should be reduced to, say, 0.015 μF or even 0.01 μF.

Combination R_{21}-C_7 determines the time needed by the gate to switch on T_6 and thus block the signal. With values as specified for these components, the time is about 50 ms, which is generally a suitable value. When a variable gate time is needed, R_{21} may be replaced by a 100 kΩ potentiometer in series with a 10 kΩ fixed resistor.

Components list

Resistors:

R_1 = 1 MΩ

R_2, R_7, R_{20}, R_{22} = 470 Ω

R_3 = 2.2 kΩ

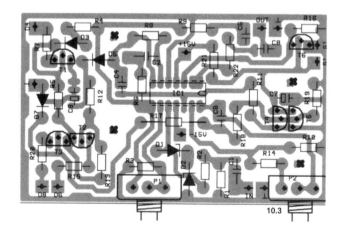

Figure 10-7. Component layout of the printed-circuit board for the noise gate. The track layout is given in the Appendix.

R_4, R_9, R_{12}, R_{18} = 4.7 kΩ

R_5, R_{13} = 22 kΩ

R_6, R_{21} = 47 kΩ

R_8 = 220 kΩ

R_{10} = 680 Ω

R_{11}, R_{16}, R_{19} = 100 kΩ

R_{11}, R_{16}, R_{19} = 100 kΩ
R_{14} = 1 kΩ
R_{15} = 820 Ω
R_{17} = 10 kΩ
P_1, P_2 = 47 kΩ log potentiometer

Capacitors:
C_1, C_6 = 0.1 μF
C_2, C_4 = 0.022 μF
C_3 = 1 μF, 16 V, radial
C_5 = 0.22 μF
C_7 = 22 μF, 16 V, radial
C_8 = 1 μ F (not electrolytic)

Semiconductors:
D_1, D_2 = zener diode 12 V, 500 mW
D_3, D_5, D_7 = 1N4148
D_4 = LED, red
D_6 = LED, green
D_8 = LERD, yellow
T_1–T_3, T_5, T_6 = BC238 or similar
T_4 = BC307 or similar

Integrated circuits:
IC_1 = TL074
Miscellaneous:
S_1 = single-pole on switch

Compander

The word compander is a contracxtion of compressor-expander, which is a noise-reduction device that compresses the dynamic range prior to recording and then expands the dynamic range by a complementary amount during playback. The circuit in Figure 10-9 consists of a compressor to reduce the dynamic range of the audio signal and an expander to increase the volume range of the audio signal. The compressor section is largely identical to that in Figure 10-4. The expander restores the dynamic range to its original value. The reason for using a compander is that the compressed signal is less susceptible to noise and similar interference. For example, the noise suppressor in a cassette deck operates on this principle. During recording with Dolby, DBX or high-com either the high frequencies alone or the entire signal are compressed. During playback, an expander restores the original dynamic range of the signal.

The present compander is eminently suitable for use as a noise suppressor in a cassette deck. During recording, the circuit must be inserted between the sound source and the cassette deck. During playback, the expander is connected to the output of the cassette deck. Another useful application of companders is as simple delay circuits, since these normally have no particularly high signal-to-noise ratio either.

Apart from use as a compander, the circuit offers a second possibility of noise suppression. In this, a filter that can be switched into the circuit (by S_1) lifts the high frequencies (pre-emphasis). In the expander section, the high fre-

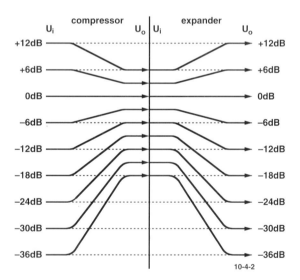

Figure 10-8.
Overall frequency
response curves of
filter R_3-C_6.

quencies are cut by the same amount (de-emphasis). The end result is the original frequency response with reduced noise. If this arrangement is used with a cassette deck, caution is needed since the additional lift of the high frequencies can lead to overload of the deck.

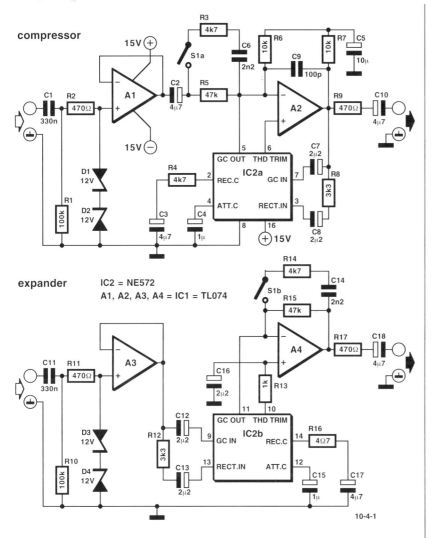

Figure 10-9.
Circuit diagram of the
compander; the upper
section is the
compressor and the
lower, the expander.

Circuit description

In the circuit diagram of the compander in Figure 10-9, the upper part is the compressor and the lower part, the expander. The compressor is virtually identical to that in Figure 10-4, except for the filter, R_3-C_6, that can be switched into circuit with S_1. At frequencies above 1.5 kHz, the reactance of C_6 is smaller than the resistance of R_5, whereupon the amplification gradually rises with in-

163

creasing frequency. At frequencies above about 15 kHz, the reactance of C_6 becomes smaller than the resistance of R_3, resulting in a levelling out of the amplification. The overall frequency response of the filter is shown in Fig ure 10-10.

The circuit of the compander is shown in the lower part of Figure 10-9. Here, IC_{2b} operates as an expander and not as compressor as in Figure 10-4. Consequently, as the name implies, it restores the original dynamic range of the audio signal. The overall changes in the frequency response made possible by the compander are shown in Figure 10-10.

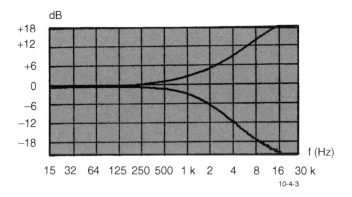

The additional filter, R_{14}-C_{14}, is located in the feedback loop of A_4.

Components list

Resistors:
R_1, R_{10} = 100 kΩ
R_2, R_9, R_{11}, R_{17} = 470 Ω
R_3, R_{14} = 4.7 kΩ, 1%
R_4, R_{16} = 4.7 Ω
R_5, R_{15} = 47 kΩ, 1%
R_6, R_7 = 10 kΩ
R_8, R_{12} = 3.3 kΩ, 1%
R_{13} = 1 kΩ

Capacitors:
C_1, C_{11} = 0.33 μF

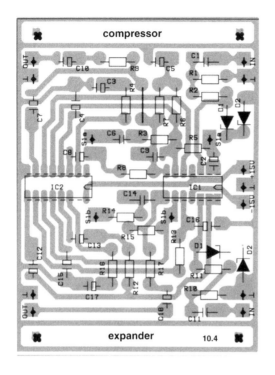

Figure 10-11. Component layout of the printed-circuit board for the compander. The track layout is given in the Appendix.

C_2, C_3, C_{10}, C_{17}, C_{18} = 4.7 μF, 16 V. radial
C_4, C_{15} = 1 μF, 16 V, radial
C_5 = 10 μF, 16 V, radial
C_6, C_{14} = 0.0022 μF, 5%
C_7, C_8, C_{12}, C_{13}, C_{16} = 2.2 μF, 16 V, radial
C_9 = 100 pF

Semiconductors:
D_1–D_4 = zener diode 12 V, 500 mW
Integrated circuits:
IC_1 = TL074
IC_2 = NE572

Miscellaneous:
S_1 = 2-pole on/off switch

165

11. Effects circuits

Effects circuits are widely used in modern music and audio systems to produce popular sound effects such as echo, reverb, chorus, and phasing in music and karaoke systems. These circuits, as are those in this section, are based on one of three electronic principles:

- non-linear distortion, such as in a distortion unit for guitars;
- variable filters, such as in phasers and wah-wah units;
- delay lines, such as in echo and chorus units.

Distortion unit for guitars

The circuit shown in Figure 11-1 provides soft distortion (as distinct from hard clipping) similar to that of a valve amplifier. The degree of distortion is set with a potentiometer. A second potentiometer matches the sound level of the distorted and undistorted audio signals. A switch enables selection of the original input signal or the distorted signal.

Figure 11-1.
Circuit diagram of the distortion unit for electric guitars.

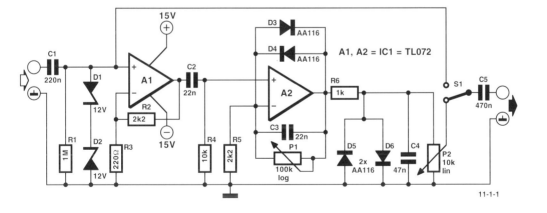

Circuit description

The input resistance of the circuit of the distortion unit in Figure 11-1 is determined by resistor R_1. The value specified (1 MΩ) enables electric guitars to be coupled directly to the circuit. Diodes D_1 and D_2 protect the input circuit against overload.

The input is applied to the non-inverting input of operational amplifier A_1 via capacitor C_1. The amplification is determined by the ratio R_2:R_1, which, with values as specified, is ×11. The output of A_1 is applied to the non-inverting input of op amp A_2 via high-pass filter R_4-C_2. The filter has a cut-off frequency of about 72 Hz.

Op amp A_2 provides more amplification, the degree of which is set with P_1. As soon as the signal exceeds a predetermined level, (germanium) diodes D_3 and D_4 clip the signal peaks which results in soft distortion. Capacitor C_3 forms a bypass for high frequencies to ensure that the distorted signal does not sound too aggressive.

Signal peaks in the output of A_2 are clipped by (germanium) diodes D_5 and D_6. Capacitor C_4 forms a bypass for high frequencies.

The sound level is set with P_2, which should be adjusted so as to equalize

Figure 11-2. Component layout of the printed-circuit board for the distortion unit. The track layout is given in the Appendix.

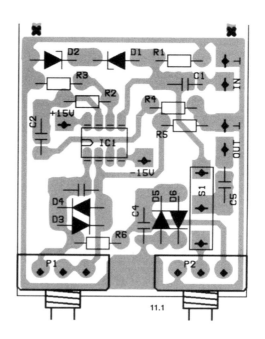

the levels of the original audio signal and the distorted signal.

The distortion effect may be switched on or off with switch S_1.

Optional modifications

Potentiometer P_1 provides a good degree of distortion, but if still more is desired, the value of R_5 may be lowered to 1 kΩ.

Components list

Resistors:
R_1 = 1 MΩ
R_2, R_5 = 2.2 kΩ
R_3 = 220 Ω
R_4 = 10 kΩ
R_6 = 1 kΩ
P_1 = 100 kΩ, log potentiometer
P_2 = 10 kΩ, linear potentiometer

Capacitors:
C_1, C_2 = 0.22 μF
C_3 = 0.022 μF
C_4 = 0.047 μF
C_5 = 0.47 μF

Semiconductors:
D_1, D_2 = zener diode 12 V, 500 mW
D_3–D_6 = AA116 or similar

Integrated circuits:
IC_1 = TL072

Miscellaneous:
S_1 = single-pole change-over switch

Distortion unit with noise gate

The distortion unit in Figure 11-3 provides a much more aggressive action than that in Figure 11-1. The amplification and degree of distortion are set with a potentiometer. Unfortunately, hard distortion of the guitar sound often results in amplified hum, noise or other interference from the guitar pick-up. These unwanted effects can, however, be eliminated by a noise gate. In the present circuit, this consists of two anti-parallel-connected diodes in the signal path. Normally, such an arrangement cannot be used because it produces distortion, but in the present circuit this does not matter. Besides, if the gate does generate unwanted interference, it can be turned off by a switch across the diodes.

A second switch enables the original audio signal or the distorted signal to be selected. When the original signal is selected, the noise gate does not function since, in view of the low amplification, noise suppression was not considered necessary.

The sound levels of the original audio signal and the distorted signal are equalized with a potentiometer.

Circuit decription

*Figure 11-3.
Circuit diagram of the
distortion unit with
noise gate.* The circuit diagram of the distortion unit with noise gate is shown in Figure 11-3. The audio signal is applied to the non-inverting input of operational amplifier A_1 via C_1 and R_2. Network C_1-R_1 is a low-pass filter with cut-

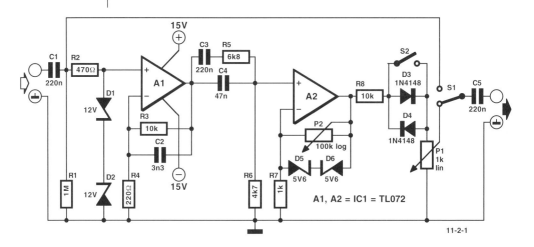

off frequency of about 20 Hz. Diodes D_1 and D_2 provide protection against overload.

Network R_3–R_6-C_2–C_4 at the output of A_1 forms a kind of bandpass filter. Capacitor C_2 attenuates frequencies above about 5 kHz; C_2 attenuates lower middle frequencies up to about 700 Hz; and C_3 attenuates the bass frequencies below about 100 Hz.

The amplification of op amp A_2 may be varied between unity and ×100. Diodes D_5 and D_6 clip the peaks of the audio signal, resulting in distortion.

The output of A_2 is applied to noise gate D_3, D_4 via resistor R_8. Only when the output exceeds 700 mV, is a signal applied to P_1. Depending on the position of switch S_1, either the original audio signal or the distorted signal is applied to the output terminals via C_5.

Optional modifications

When distortion control P_2 is full clockwise (open), it may happen that hum or other interference is amplified to such a degree that the noise gate is actu-

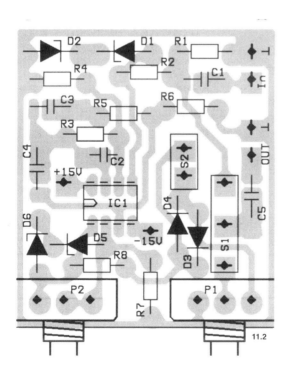

Figure 11-4.
Component layout of the printed-circuit board for the distortion unit with noise gate. The track layout is given in the Appendix.

ated. This may be remedied by two diodes in series in both the D_3 and D_4 positions (that is, a total of four diodes).

Components list
Resistors:
$R_1 = 1\ M\Omega$
$R_2 = 470\ \Omega$
$R_3, R_8 = 10\ k\Omega$
$R_4 = 220\ \Omega$
$R_5 = 6.8\ k\Omega$
$R_6 = 4.7\ k\Omega$
$R_7 = 1\ k\Omega$
$P_1 = 1\ k\Omega$, linear potentiometer
$P_2 = 100\ k\Omega$, log potentiometer

Capacitors:
$C_1, C_3, C_5 = 0.22\ \mu F$
$C_2 = 0.0033\ \mu F$
$C_4 = 0.047\ \mu F$

Semiconductors:
$D_1, D_2 = $ zener diode, 12 V, 500 mW
$D_3, D_4 = $ 1N4148
$D_5, D_6 = $ zener diode, 5.6 V, 500 mW

Integrated circuits:
$IC_1 = $ TL072

Miscellaneous:
$S_1 = $ single-pole change-over switch
$S_2 = $ single-pole on/off switch

Phaser

A traditional phaser is an effects unit in which the notches of a comb filter are slowly swept up and down the audio band to produce a pleasant effect on music signals. In the present circuit, a different approach is used: four poten-

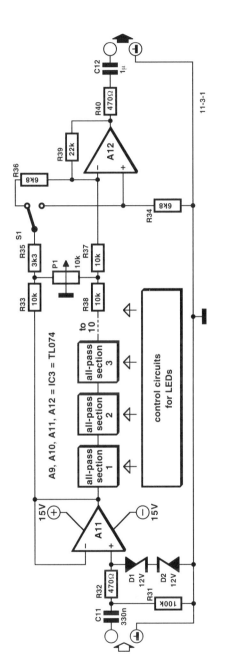

Figure 11-5.
Circuit diagram of the
phaser.

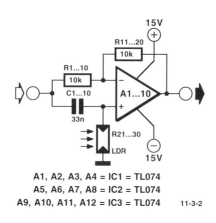

Figure 11-6. Circuit diagram of a single all-pass filter used in Figure 11-5.

A1, A2, A3, A4 = IC1 = TL074
A5, A6, A7, A8 = IC2 = TL074
A9, A10, A11, A12 = IC3 = TL074   11-3-2

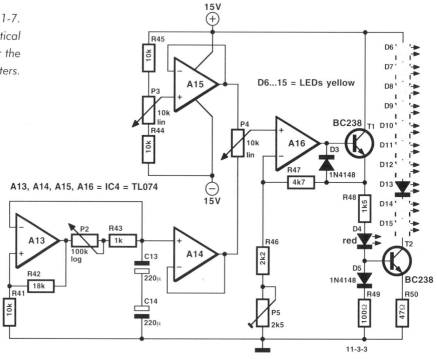

Figure 11-7. Diagram of the optical control circuit for the all-pass filters.

D6...15 = LEDs yellow

A13, A14, A15, A16 = IC4 = TL074

11-3-3

tiometers and a switch enable a number of phase shifts to be obtained. The original signal is mixed with the phase-shifted signal. When potentiometer P_1 (Figure 11-5) is turned fully anticlockwise, only the original signal appears at the output terminals. When the control is set to the centre of its travel, the original and phase-shifted signal are mixed in a ratio of 1:1, which gives the typical phaser effect. When the control is turned fully clockwise, only the phase-shifted signal appears at the output terminals. In this condition, the slowly changing phase shift produces a sort of phase modulation.

Control P_4 enables manual or automatic modulation of the phase-shifted signal. When the control is set fully anticlockwise, the phase shift is varied by a triangular-wave generator. When it is turned fully clockwise, the phase shift may be varied manually with P_3. When P_4 is at its mid-position, the automatic modulation of the phase shift occurs for only half the range; the other half can be set manually.

The frequency of the triangular-wave generator is set with P_2. The further this control is turned clockwise, the lower the frequency, and thus the phase shift and the phaser effect.

Before any mixing takes place, the original signal can be inverted with S_1 to produce an inverted frequency response.

Circuit description

The circuit diagram of the phaser is divided into three: Figure 11-5 shows the entire circuit; Figure 11-6 one of the three all-pass filters shown as a box in 11-6; and Figure 11-7 shows the optical control circuit of the all-pass filters.

The audio input signal is applied to the non-inverting input of impedance converter A_{11} via C_{11} and R_{32}. Network C_{11}-R_{31} is a low-pass filter with a cut-off frequency of about 30 Hz. Diodes D_1 and D_2 protect the circuit against overload.

The output of A_{11} is fed to control P_1 via R_{33} and also to a comb filter, consisting of all-pass sections 1–10. The original signal is available at the junction of P_1 and R_{33}, and the phase-shifted signal at the junction of R_{38} and R_{37}. Depending on the setting of P_1, either of these signals is wholly or partially short-circuited. When this control is in its mid-position, both signals are attenuated slightly. The phase-shifted signal is applied to, and inverted by, op amp A_{12} via R_{37}. The original audio signal is available at the pole of S_1. When this switch is in the position shown, the signal is also inverted and amplified by A_{12}. When S_1 is linked to R_{34}, however, the signal is amplified but not inverted. In other words, with S_1 in the position shown, A_{12} operates an inverting adder and with the switch in the other position, as a differential amplifier.

The circuit of one of the ten all-pass sections is shown in Figure 11-6. The filter is controlled by a light-dependent resistor: the requisite light is provided by ten light-emitting diodes. In theory, the control could be effected by field-effect transistors (FETs), but these do not have a linear resistance, which LDRs have.

Figure 11-8.
Component layout of
the printed-circuit
board for the phaser.
The track layout is
given in the Appendix.

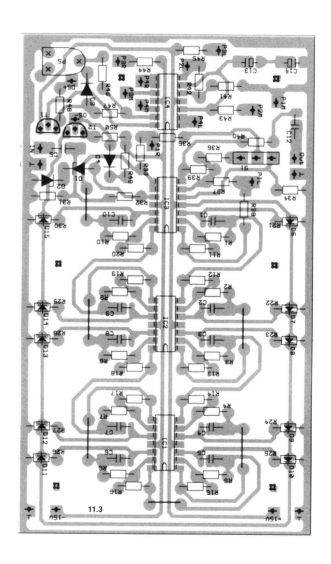

The light-generating circuit is shown in Figure 11-7. Operational amplifier A_{13} and associated components is a triangular-wave generator whose frequency is determined by the setting of P_2. Op amp A_{14} is an impedance converter, while A_{15}, in conjunction with R_{44}, R_{45} and P_3 generates a voltage that can be varied from -5 V to $+5$ V. The setting of P_4 determines whether the manual signal, the output signal of A_{13}, or both are to be used for control purposes.

Operational amplifier A_{16} functions as a non-inverting amplifier with an amplification of about $\times 2.5$. Transistor T_1 raises the level of the output current of the op amp, resulting in the variable ± 5 V being raised to about ± 12 V. At the same time, a voltage of 3–27 V is derived from the -15 V line. Consequently, a current of 0–15 mA flows through the series network R_{48}-R_{49}-D_4-D_5. Since the value of R_{50} is exactly half that of R_{49}, transistor T_2 provides a current of 0–30 mA for diodes D_6–D_{15}. Each of the ten LEDs drives one of the LDRs in the all-pass filters. Diode D_4, however, is mounted at the front panel to make it visible as an optical check for the user.

Components list

Resistors:
R_1–R_{20}, R_{33}, R_{37}, R_{38}, R_{41}, R_{44}, $R_{45} = 10$ kΩ, 1%
R_{21}–R_{30} = light-dependent resistor (see text)
$R_{31} = 100$ kΩ
R_{32}, $R_{40} = 470$ Ω
R_{34}, $R_{36} = 6.8$ kΩ, 1%
$R_{35} = 3.3$ kΩ, 1%
$R_{39} = 22$ kΩ, 1%
$R_{42} = 18$ kΩ, 1%
$R_{43} = 1$ kΩ
$R_{46} = 2.2$ kΩ
$R_{47} = 4.7$ kΩ
$R_{48} = 1.5$ kΩ, 1.5 W
$R_{49} = 100$ Ω
$R_{50} = 47$ Ω
$P_1 = 10$ kΩ, linear potentiometer
$P_2 = 100$ kΩ, log potentiometer
P_3, $P_4 = 10$ kΩ, linear potentiometer
$P_5 = 2.5$ kΩ preset

Capacitors:
C_1–C_{10} = 0.033 μF
C_{11} = 0.33 μF
C_{12} = 1 μF (not electrolytic)
C_{13}, C_{14} = 220 μF, 10 V, radial

Semiconductors:
D_1, D_2 = zener diode, 12 V, 500 mW
D_3, D_5 = 1N4148
D_4 = LED, red
D_6–D_{15} = LED, yellow, 5 mm
T_1, T_2 = BC238 or similar
Integrated circuits:
IC_1–IC_4 = TL074

Miscellaneous:
S_1 = single-pole change-over switch

*Figure 11-9.
Two ways of ensuring
correct optical coup-
ling between the light-
dependent resistor and
the light-emitting
diode.*

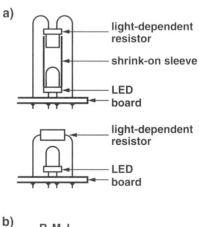

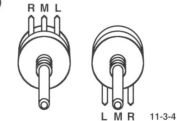

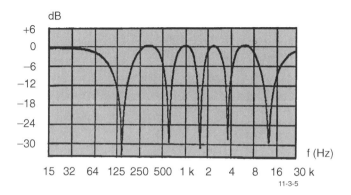

Figure 11-10.
Frequency response
when the LEDs light at
average brightness.

Construction notes

Light-dependent resistors (LDRs) are available in many shapes, sizes and values. Almost all of these are suitable for use in the phaser. To ensure that the all-pass sections are driven correctly, each LDR must be optically coupled to the associated LED. There are several ways of doing so, of which two are shown in Figure 11-9. The best and perhaps easier of the two is to put the two associated components together in a length of black heat-shrinkable sleeving. This has the advantage that the LDR cannot be affected by spurious light. The sleeving should not be shrunk too much since this may adversely affect the optical coupling.

In contrast to other constructions in this book, the potentiometers in the phaser are not soldered directly to the printed-circuit board, but fitted on the front panel and linked to the board by short lengths of insulated circuit wire. The three terminals for this purpose are marked L(eft). M(id-position) and R(ight). See Figure 11-9B.

Calibration

To ensure that the phaser operates correctly, control P_5 must be calibrated. For this purpose, turn P_4 fully clockwise and P_3 fully anticlockwise, and adjust P_5 until the red control LED just lights faintly.

12. Output stages

Audio-frequency output stages are intended to raise small signals of the order of a few hundred millivolts to a level of a few volts. The signal-to-noise ratio should be large and the distortion, small. The output impedance should be small: of the order of a few hundred milliohms. Loudspeakers with an input impedance of 4 Ω or 8 Ω are thus overmatched, which ensures that the output voltage of the amplifier does not vary with the applied load. It should be noted that the rating '4 Ω' or '8 Ω' stated on an output amplifier does not refer to its output impedance but to the permissible load.

Principle of operation

Figure 12-1a shows the circuit of the simplest possible amplifier. Resistor R_1 provides the transistor with a small base current. The resulting collector current is, ideally, large enough to ensure that the potential across the load resistance, R_L, is equal to half the supply voltage, U_B. The other half of the supply voltage is dropped across the collector-emitter junction of the transistor. The additional current provided by an input signal alters the voltage ratio, as may be seen in Figure 12-1b. This shows the variation in the potential across R_L between U_B and 0 V when a sinusoidal signal is applied to the input of the circuit.

The type of of circuit just discussed is frequently used in preamplifiers, but does not lend itself to output amplifiers, since the potential across the load is

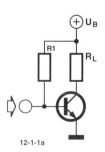

12-1-1a

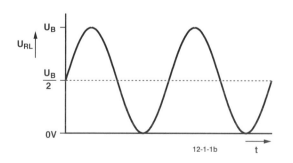

12-1-1b

Figure 12-1.
Circuit of a basic voltage amplifier and the resulting waveform when a sinusoidal signal is applied to the input.

always half the supply voltage, even in the absence of an incoming signal. This would be harmful for the loudspeakers and also result in an unnecessarily high current drain.

Figure 12-2.
Diagram of a simple push-pull amplifier and the resulting voltage across the load when a sinusoidal signal is applied to the input.

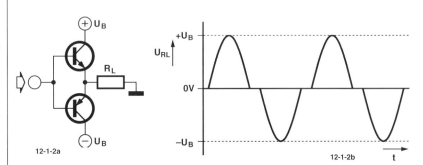

Much better suited to output amplifiers is the push-pull stage in Figure 12-2a. In the absence of an input signal, both transistors are cut off. When a signal greater than +700 mV is applied, the upper transistor is switched on and operates as impedance converter; when a signal greater than −700 mV is applied, the lower transistor conducts and functions as impedance converter. When the applied voltage is smaller than ±700 mV, the circuit remains quiescent. The waveform in Figure 12-2b shows the voltage across the load when a sinusoidal signal is applied to the input of the circuit. Note the distortion at the zero crossings of the waveform, which is caused by the circuit remaining inoperative when the input signal is smaller than ±700 mV. It is clear that this amplifier cannot be used in an hi-fi equipment.

A much sounder approach is given by the push-pull amplifier in Figure 12-3. In this circuit, a 1.5 V voltage source provides the requisite base bias for both transistors, which ensures that there is no (or hardly any) zero crossing distortion. Theoretically, each transistor needs a base bias of about 700 mV, giving a total of 1.4 V. However, the actual requirement is for 1.41 V; the difference of 10 mV drops across the two emitter resistors. Nevertheless, the quiescent current drawn by the circuit is relatively small: here, of the order of 20 mA. The two emitter resistors are essential: without them, the quiescent current would rise to a couple of amperes.

In practical circuits, there is, of course, no separate voltage source. Figure 12-4 shows a frequently used configuration in which the base bias is generated by the circuit itself. The part of the circuit enclosed by the dashed lines functions

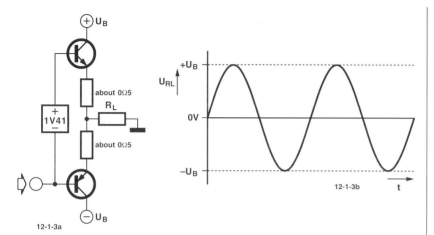

Figure 12-3.
Push-pull amplifier
with a fixed base-bias-
voltage source.

as a variable zener diode, that is, one whose rated voltage may be varied.
Most output amplifiers are based on the configuration in Figure 12-4.

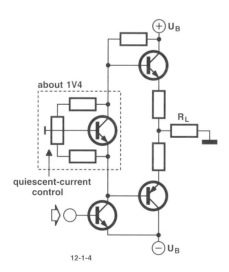

Figure 12-4.
Push-pull amplifier
with self-generated
base bias voltages.

Simple 6-watt stereo amplifier

For the design and construction of low-power output amplifiers, there is an interesting integrated circuit available, Type A210K, which is supplied mounted on a small aluminium heat sink. The IC has an integrated thermal overload protection that comes into operation at about 130 °C. Only a handful of passive components are required to turn the IC into a small 2×6 W stereo output amplifier, as shown in Figure 12-5.

Figure 12-5.
Circuit diagram of the
simple 2×6 W stereo
output amplifier.

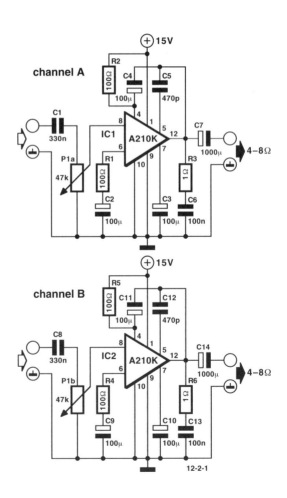

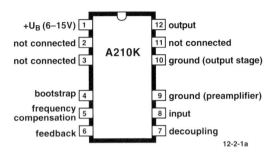

Figure 12-6.
Pinout of the Type
A210K integrated
circuit.

Pin labels (left side): +U$_B$ (6–15V) [1], not connected [2], not connected [3], bootstrap [4], frequency compensation [5], feedback [6].

A210K

Pin labels (right side): [12] output, [11] not connected, [10] ground (output stage), [9] ground (preamplifier), [8] input, [7] decoupling.

12-2-1a

Circuit description

The following description will refer to (left-hand) channel A only: that of (right-hand) channel B is identical; only the component references are different. In Figure 12-5, the stereo input signal is applied to the input of IC$_1$ via capacitor C$_1$ and potentiometer P$_{1a}$. Resistor R$_1$ and capacitor C$_2$ are part of the feedback loop. The smaller the value of R$_1$, the higher the amplification of the IC. Capacitor C$_3$ smooths the supply voltage to the preamplifiers in the IC and suppresses any residual hum on the supply lines. Network R$_2$-C$_4$ form a Bootstrap circuit. As soon as a positive half-wave appears at the output of the IC, C$_4$ raises the level at pin 4 above that of the supply voltage. This arrangement enables the output voltage to be driven a little higher than without the bootstrap. Resistor R$_3$ and capacitors C$_5$, C$_6$ provide the necessary frequency compensation and suppress any oscillations in the ultrasonic range.

In the absence of an input signal, the output voltage of the IC is a direct one of about half the supply voltage, so that an incoming signal can be driven to the same extent positively and negatively. The direct output voltage is decoupled by C$_7$ to ensure a clean audio signal to the loudspeakers.

Power supply

In contrast to virtually all other circuits in this book, the power supply described in Chapter 5 cannot be used with the 6-watt stereo output amplifier for two reasons: firstly, it cannot provide sufficient current, and secondly, the stereo amplifier does not need a symmetrical power supply.

Since the stereo amplifier provides a total output power of about 12 watts, the power supply must be capable of providing some 20 watts, since the efficiency of push-pull output amplifiers is about 60%. This means, of course, that about 8 watts is dissipated as heat.

The supply voltage must be about 15 V, but must not exceed 20 V in the ab-

Figure 12-7.
Circuit of a suitable
power supply for the
6-watt stereo output
amplifier.

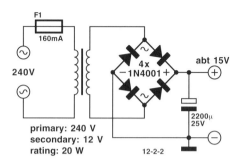

sence of an incoming audio signal. The IC can operate from a supply voltage as low as 6 V, but it provides its maximum power output only at a higher voltage, of course.

The circuit diagram of a suitable power supply is shown in Figure 12-7.

Optional modifications

The amplification of the amplifier depends on the values of resistors R_1 and R_4. If a higher amplification than specified is required, these resistors may be replaced by 56 Ω types. If this is done, the value of capacitors C_2 and C_9 should be raised to 220 μF.

If a lower limit of the bass range is desired, the value of capacitors C_7 and C_{14} should be raised to 2200 μF.

Figure 12-8.
Component layout of
the printed-circuit
board for the stereo
output amplifier. The
track layout is given in
the Appendix.

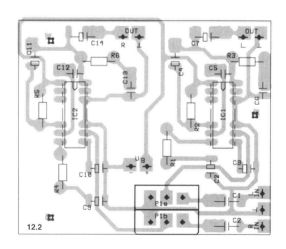

Components list

Resistors:
R_1, R_2, R_4, R_5 = 100 Ω
R_3, R_6 = 1 Ω
P_1 = stereo potentiometer, 2×50 (or 2×47) kΩ. logarithmic

Capacitors:
C_1, C_8 = 0.33 μF
C_2–C_4, C_9–C_{11} = 100 μF, 16 V, radial
C_5, C_{12} = 470 pF
C_6, C_{13} = 0.1 μF
C_7, C_{14} = 1000 μF or 2200 μF, 16 V, radial

Integrated circuits:
IC_1, IC_2 = A210K

General-purpose output amplifier

The amplifier discussed in this section can produce output powers from 20 watts to 100 watts, depending on the values of certain components. The use of darlington transistors keeps the number of components down. Because of certain circuit refinements, the efficiency is rather higher than is usual with this kind of amplifier and setting the quiescent current level is not necessary.

Circuit description

In Figure 12-9, transistors T_1 and T_2 form a differential amplifier. The potential at the base of T_2 is compared with the input voltage (at the base of T_1). When the base voltage of T_2 is higher than that of T_1, T_1 is on, since the potential across its base-emitter junction is about 700 mV, whereas that of T_2 is slightly lower (so that T_2 cannot conduct). The base of T_3 is then driven by T_1, so that T_3 is also on and connects the bases of T_4 and T_5 to ground: the output of the circuit then drops. Since the output is dropped across potential divider R_4-R_5, it drives the base of T_2. Consequently, the base potential of T_2, which at the onset was slightly higher than that of T_1, drops until the base voltages of the differential amplifier are equal. This kind of operation is basically identical to that of an operational amplifier with feedback. This means that the circuit controls the output voltage so that the base potentials of T_1 and T_2 are identical. The ratio

Figure 12-9.
Circuit diagram of the
general-purpose
output amplifier.

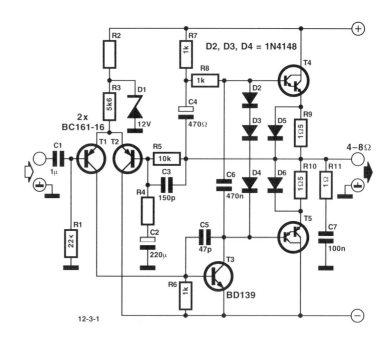

of resistors R_4 and R_5 determines the amplification of the circuit.

Diode D_1 and resistor R_2 hold the voltage at the upper end of R_3 stable at about 12 V to ensure that any hum on the supply lines is suppressed. Diodes D_2–D_4 generate the requisite base bias voltage for the darlington transistors. The value of emitter resistors R_9 and R_{10} is relatively high, which makes setting the quiescent current unnecessary. To keep the dissipation in the emitter resistors low, diodes D_5 and D_6 ensure that the maximum voltage drop across

Figure 12-10.
Frequency response of
the general-purpose
output amplifier.

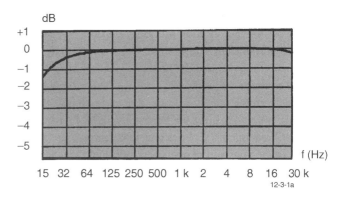

them cannot exceed 700 mV.

Network R_7-R_8-C_4 is a bootstrap circuit which ensures that when, for example, the base voltage of T_4 rises by 10 V, the output voltage of the circuit rises by the same amount. Capacitor C_4 raises the voltage at the junction of R_7 and R_8 also by 10 V. This means that the potential at both ends of R_8 is lifted by the same amount, so that the drop across the resistor, and the current through it, remain unchanged irrespective of the output voltage.

Capacitors C_3, C_5, C_6, C_7 and resistor R_{11} are not part of the operation of the circuit: they serve merely to suppress any spurious oscillations.

Component values

The circuit can be built as a 20-W, 40-W, 60-W, 80-W or 100-W amplifier. The output power depends entirely on the value of R_2 and R_4, on the type of transistor used for T_4 and T_5, and on the level of the supply voltage. Obviously, the heat sinks must also match the power output. All these factors are summarized in the Table 12-1.

	Power output				
	20 W	40 W	60 W	80 W	100 W
Supply voltage	±15 V	±20 V	±24.5 V	±28 V	±32 √
T_4	TIP120	TIP120	TIP130	TIP141	TIP141
T_5	TIP125	TIP125	TIP135	TIP146	TIP146
R_2	470 Ω	1.2 kΩ	1.8 kΩ	2.7 kΩ	3.3 kΩ
R_4	390 Ω	270 Ω	220 Ω	180 Ω	180 Ω
Heat sink	8 K W^{-1}	4 K W^{-1}	2.7 K W^{-1}	2 K W^{-1}	1.6 K W^{-1}

Table 12-1. Correlation between output power, supply voltage and various properties of components used.

Construction

Transistors T_4 and T_5 must be isolated from the heat sink: they should be soldered directly to the printed-circuit board or via short lengths of circuit wire. The relevant rating of the heat sink is given in the table. The thermal resistance quoted shows by how many kelvin (degree Celsius) the temperature of the heat sink rises for each watt of output. For instance, if an 80-W amplifier is built, the temperature of the heat sink used must not rise by more than 160 K.

Transistor T_3 must be soldered in place with its metal surface pointing towards R_6.

Figure 12-11.
Circuit diagram of
general-purpose
power supply.

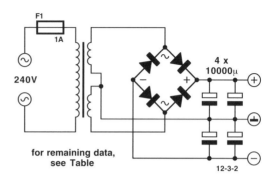

for remaining data,
see Table

12-3-2

Power supply

The rating of the transformer, rectifier and smoothing capacitors must be in accordance with the output power of the amplifier as shown in Table 12-2. The circuit of a power supply suitable for powering the general-purpose output amplifier is shown in Figure 12-11.

Table 12-2.
Correlation between
supply voltage,
transformer voltage
and rating, rectifier
current, and capacitor
rating.

	Power output				
	20 W	40 W	60 W	80 W	100 W
Supply voltage	±15 V	±20 V	±24.5 V	±28 V	±32 √
Transf. voltage	2×12 V	2×15 V	2×18 V	2×21 V	2×24 V
Transf. rating	30 W	60 W	90 W	120 W	150 W
Rectifier current	1.3 A	2 A	2.5 A	2.9 A	3.3 A
Capacitor rating	20 V	25 V	30 V	35 V	40 V

If the amplifier is built as a stereo version, that is, two amplifiers as in Figure 12-9, the transformer rating and rectifier current must, of course, be doubled. If, in an emergency, the transformer rating is rather lower than specified, it can be used and the music power output remains unchanged. However, the output of a sinusoidal signal is reduced somewhat.

Optional modifications

The value of R_4 determines the amplification of the circuit. Its values given in Table 12-1 are calculated to give full output power when the input signal is 500 mV. When a higher amplification is needed, the value of R_4 may be reduced within reason. Conversely, increasing the value of the resistor reduces the amplification.

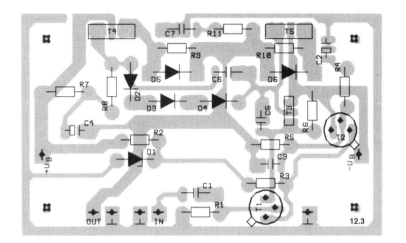

Figure 12-12.
Component layout of
the printed-circuit
board for the general-
purpose output
amplifier. The track
layout is given in the
Appendix.

Components list

Resistors:

R_1 = 22 kΩ

R_2 = see Table 12-1

R_3 = 5.6 kΩ

R_4 = see Table 12-1

R_5 = 10 kΩ

R_6 = 1 kΩ

R_7, R_8 = 1 kΩ, 0.5 W

R_9, R_{10} = 1.5 Ω

Capacitors:

C_1 = 1 μF (not electrolytic)

C_2 = 220 μF, 10 V, radial

C_3 = 150 pF

C_4 = 470 μF, 35 V, radial

C_5 = 47 pF

C_6 = 0.47 μF

C_7 = 0.1 μF

Semiconductors:

D_1 = zener diode, 12 V, 500 mW

D_2–D_4 = 1N4148

D_5, D_6 = power diode P600A (6 A) or similar
T_1, T_2 = BC161-16
T_3 = BD139
T_4, T_5 = see Table 12-1

Miscellaneous:
Heat sink for T_4, T_5 = see Table 12-1
Isolating materials for T_4, T_5 (washers, bushes, heat conducting paste)

13. Headphone amplifiers

The simplest way of driving a pair of headphones is to tap the signal from a suitable point (normally the output terminals) in the output amplifier. To ensure that the headphones will not be overloaded, two resistors, or four in case of a stereo signal, are needed—see Figure 13-1. Unfortunately, an output amplifier is not always available as, for instance, in a control panel or preamplifier. In such cases, a dedi-

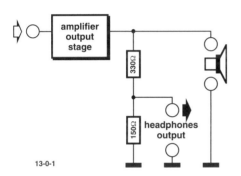

13-0-1

Figure 13-1.
One way of deriving a headphones output from an output amplifier with the aid of two resistors.

cated headphone amplifier must be built.

Impedance and matching

When hi-fi circuits are to be interlinked, overmatching is used in nearly all cases. In overmatching, the output impedance of a circuit is much smaller than the input impedance of the following circuit to which it is to be linked. For instance, the output impedance of output amplifiers is normally smaller than an ohm, whereas the input impedance of the loudspeakers is 4 Ω or 8 Ω. Headphones normally have an input impedance of between 16 Ω and 600 Ω. The output impedance of headphone amplifiers also varies from a few ohms to 500 Ω. Therefore, depending on their impedance and the output impedance of headphone amplifiers, headphones are used in current, power or voltage matching. There are no standards for this. Note, however, that most top-quality headphone amplifiers have a relatively low output impedance, which is beneficial to the frequency response and transients fidelity. On the other hand, high-impedance headphones are much less sensitive than low-impedance types. A fairly constant sound level is obtained with units that have an output impedance of about 100 ohms.

Simple stereo headphone amplifier

This section describes a simple, easy-to-build headphone amplifier for use with stereo equipment. The output power is provided by four parallel-connected operational amplifiers per channel. This approach avoids the use of special ICs and transistors.

Figure 13-2. Circuit diagram of the stereo headphone amplifier.

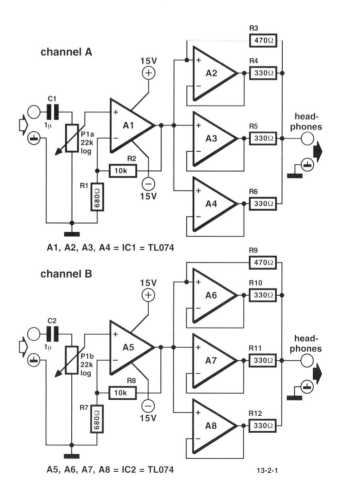

The sound level is varied with the aid of a stereo potentiometer. The output impedance is about 90 Ω per channel.

Circuit description

In the circuit of the headphone amplifier (Figure 13-2), the left-hand and right-hand channels, A and B respectively, are identical; in the following description will refer to channel A only.

The input signal is applied to the non-inverting input of op amp A_1 via C_1 and potentiometer P_{1a}. The amplification factor is determined by the values of R_1 and R_2. With values as specified, it is about ×16.

Op amps A_2 to A_4 are configured as impedance converters, so that the output signals of all four op amps are identical. These signals are combined into a common, more powerful signal for the headphones via R_3–R_6. Resistor R_3 has a slightly higher value than the other three. This arrangement prevents A_1 from being prematurely overdriven. Note that overdriving A_1 will adversely affect the other three op amps. The output impedance of the amplifier is fairly accurately the composite of the four parallel-connected resistors and is about 90 ohms.

Optional modifications

The value of resistors R_1, R_2, R_7 and R_8 has been calculated to afford satisfactory amplification even with weak input signals. When with a normal audio input the volume control is opened fully, the headphones will, of course, be overloaded. If reduced amplification is desired, the value of R_1 and R_7 should be increased to 1 kΩ

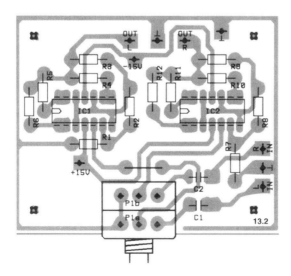

Figure 13-3.
Component layout of the printed-circuit board for the stereo headphone amplifier. The track layout is given in the Appendix.

or even 1.5 kΩ.

Components list

Resistors:

$R_1, R_7 = 680\ \Omega$

$R_2, R_8 = 10\ k\Omega$

$R_3, R_9 = 470\ \Omega$

$R_4–R_6, R_{10}–R_{12} = 330\ \Omega$

P_1 = stereo potentiometer, 2×20 (or 2×22) kΩ, logarithmic

Capacitors:

$C_1, C_2 = 1\ \mu F$ (not electrolytic)

Integrated circuits:

IC_1, IC_2 = TL074

High-power headphone amplifier

The headphone amplifier described in this section lends itself particularly to use in

Figure 13-4.
Circuit diagram of
the high-power
headphone amplifier

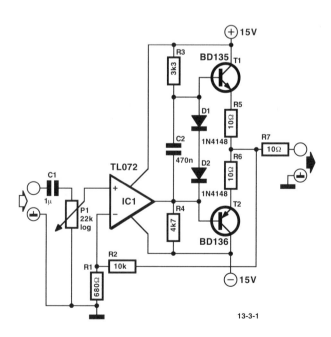

196

mixers and similar applications where a a high audio output is needed, much higher than that provided by the amplifier in the previous section. Moreover, its output impedance of 10 Ω is appreciably lower, enabling several headphones to be connected to it simultaneously. If only mono(phonic) signals are to be processed, both receivers (earpieces) of the headphones are connected to the output terminals. To process stereo(phonic) signals, two amplifiers need to be built side by side.

Circuit description

The circuit of the amplifier (Figure 13-4) consists of a simple operational amplifier that feeds a complementary transistor output amplifier. The bias for the transistors is derived from network R_3-D_1-D_2. In view of the relatively high value of the emitter resistors quiescent current setting is not needed.

The feedback via R_2 is not taken from the op amp output, but from the output of the transistors, so that any distortion there is reduced appreciably.

The amplification of the circuit is determined by the ratio R_1:R_2. At full drive, it is about ×16.

Construction

Populating the printed-circuit board in Figure 13-4 should not present any undue difficulties. Note, however, that transistors T_1 and T_2 must be located so that their metallic side points to the centre of the board.

If the amplifier is built in duplicate for stereo applications, P_1 may be replaced

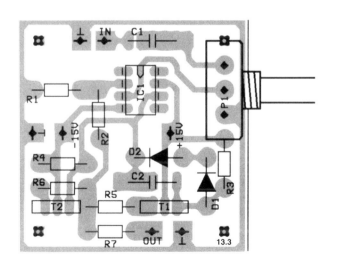

Figure 13-5. Component layout of the printed-circuit board for the high-power headphone amplifier. The track layout is given in the Appendix.

by a stereo version that is linked to the boards by short lengths of circuit wire.

Caution

The amplifier can produce such a high sound level, particularly when low-impedance headphones are used, that at full volume the eardrums may be damaged. It is therefore advisable to turn the volume control fully anticlockwise before putting the headphones over the ears and then turn up the volume as required.

Note that the rating of the mains transformer in the power supply need not exceed 3 watts.

Components list

Resistors:
$R_1 = 680\,\Omega$
$R_2 = 10\,k\Omega$
$R_3 = 3.3\,k\Omega$
$R_4 = 4.7\,k\Omega$
$R_5, R_6, R_7 = 10\,\Omega$
$P_1 = 22\,k\Omega$ logarithmic

Capacitors:
$C_1 = 1\,\mu F$ (not electrolytic)
$C_2 = 0.47\,\mu F$

Semiconductors:
$D_1, D_2 = 1N4148$
$T_1 = BD135$
$T_2 = BD136$

Integrated circuits:
$IC_1 = TL071$

14. Special circuits

This chapter deals with some special circuits that cannot be used as preamplifier, filter or effect unit.

Stereo wideband control

Radio cassette players are often provided with a stereo wideband-effect control, which normally allows switching between mono, stereo, and stereo wideband. In the stereo wideband position, part of the right-hand stereo signal is inverted and added to the left-hand channel and part of the left-hand signal is inverted and added to the right-hand channel. The inversion is the special property of this arrangement, which makes it appear as if the distance between the left-hand and right-hand loudspeakers has been increased. This makes the music sound a little more spacious and fuller-bodied.

The wideband control in this section does more than the one used in consumer products, because it does not use a switch but a potentiometer that provides seamless control from mono (full anticlockwise) through stereo (centre position) to stereo wideband operation (fully clockwise).

Circuit description

The circuit diagram of the stereo wideband control is shown in Figure 14-1. The circuit proper consists of amplifiers A_3 to A_6, while stages A_1 and A_2 are impedance converters with overvoltage protection and direct-voltage decoupling at the input.

Op amp A_3 functions as a differential amplifier in which the left-hand (L) signal is deducted from the right-hand (R) signal. The output of A_3 is, therefore, a signal R–L. Op amp A_4 functions as an inverting adder that has an amplification of about ×0.5. The output of this stage is, therefore, –0.5L–0.5R.

Op amp A_5 also functions as an inverting adder that converts the –0.5L–0.5R signal into a signal 0.5L+0.5R, which is derived from the usual mono signal L+R. When P_1 is turned clockwise, A_5 is also fed with the signal R–L from A_3. When the potentiometer is at the centre of its travel, the signal from A_3 is halved, that is, 0.5R–0.5L, which is inverted by A_5 into 0.5L–0.5R. When this is added to the mono signal (across R_{16}), the result is 0.5L–0.5R+0.5L+0.5R = L. When the potentiometer is fully clock-

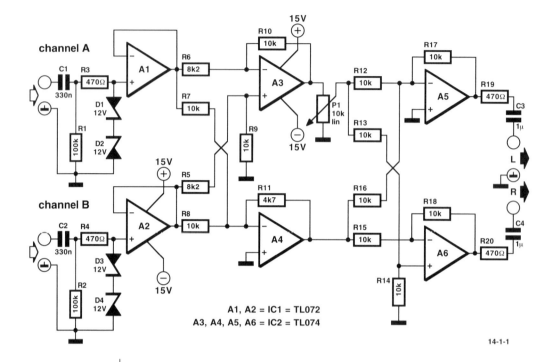

channel A

channel B

15V

A1, A2 = IC1 = TL072
A3, A4, A5, A6 = IC2 = TL074

14-1-1

wise, the signal at the output of A_5 is $L-R+0.5L+0.5R = 1.5L-0.5R$.

Op amp A_6 operates as a differential amplifier. When the potentiometer is fully anticlockwise, this stage provides the same signal as A_5, that is, $0.5L+0.5R$. With P_1 in its centre position, the signal is $0.5L+0.5R+0.5R-0.5L = R$. When P_1 is turned fully clockwise, the signal is $0.5L+0.5R+R-L = 1.5R-0.5L$.

Construction
Potentiometer P_1 must not be soldered directly to the printed-circuit board, but linked to it by short lengths of insulated circuit wire. The relevant terminals are marked P1L, P1M, and P1R, signifying anticlockwise, centre position and clockwise respectively.

Components list
Resistors:
$R_1, R_2 = 100 \text{ k}\Omega$
$R_3, R_4, R_{19}, R_{20} = 470 \ \Omega$
$R_5, R_6 = 8.2 \text{ k}\Omega, 1\%$

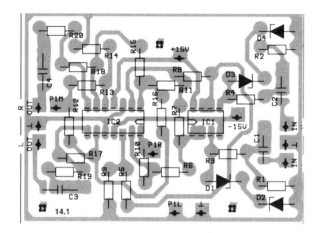

Figure 14-2.
Component layout of
the printed-circuit
board for the wide-
band control. The
track layout is given in
the Appendix.

R_7–R_{10}, R_{12}–R_{18} = 10 kΩ, 1%
R_{11} = 4.7 kΩ
P_1 = 10 kΩ, linear

Capacitors:
C_1, C_2 = 0.33 μF
C_3, C_4 = 1 μF

Semiconductors:
D_1–D_4 = zener diode, 12 V, 500 mW

Integrated circuits:
IC_1 = TL072
IC_2 = TL074

Playback unit

This is a circuit especially designed for karaoke fans: it converts a standard stereo
music signal into a playback signal without vocal content. The built-in microphone
amplifier enables you to sing in accord with the playback music.

The design of the circuit is based on a designer's trick. The circuit derives from the
standard stereo signal a differential signal (right-hand less left-hand). This results
in all parts of the signal that are identical in the two channels cancelling each other

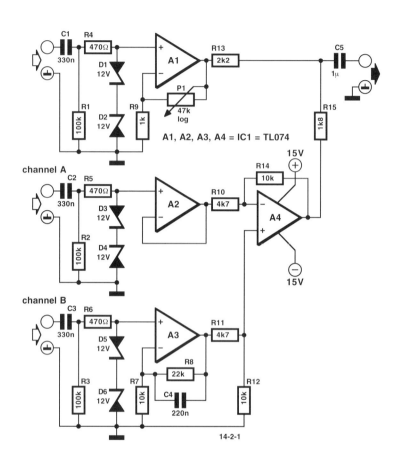

Figure 14-3.
Circuit diagram of the
playback unit.

out. Although the orchestral instruments are normally spatially spread out, singing is usually performed at the centre microphone. This means that the vocal content in the left-hand channel is invariably the same as that in the right-hand channel. If, therefore, one channel is subtracted from the other, there is nothing, or very little, left of the singing voices.

Of course, in practice this does not always work out so well. For instance, cassette recordings are normally not very suitable, but compact disks (CDs) generally are. Nevertheless, even then fragments of the original singing remain audible. Also, the reverberation of singing is often true stereo. Another problem is that sometimes it is not just the singing that is recorded via the central mcirophone(s). A guitar solo, for instance, is frequently recorded via the central microphone(s) also. It all means that you have to try out which recordings lend themselves to use with the present unit. In the present circuit, the sound from bass instruments (which are also often centred) is given a boost in the right-hand channel, so that during the subtraction of the left-hand channel the bass frequencies are not cancelled, but merely slightly attenuated.

Circuit description

The circuit diagram of the playback unit is shown in Figure 14-3. The left-hand signal is applied to operational amplifier A_2, which functions as an impedance converter, via decoupling network R_2-C_2 and overvoltage protection network R_5-D_4-D_5. The right-hand channel is applied to op amp A_3 also via a decoupling network (R_3-C_3) and an overvoltage protection network (R_6-D_5-D_6). Op amp A_3 has a filter in its feedback loop. Capacitor C_4 has a low reactance for middle and high frequencies, so that the op amp functions as an impedance converter. However, at bass frequencies, C_4 and resistor R_7 form a potential divider, so that the amplification rises. For very low frequencies, the amplification is limited to ×3 by R_8.

The outputs of A_2 and A_3 are combined and applied to A_4, which operates as a differential amplifier. This stage therefore produces a signal R–L, whereby all signal parts that are identical in the two channels are eliminated or very nearly so. The bass frequencies are retained, however, owing to filter R_7-R_8-C_4.

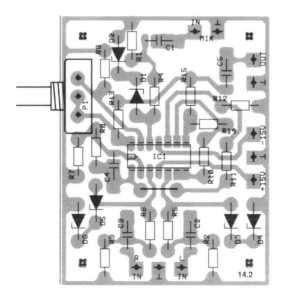

Figure 14-4.
Component layout of the printed-circuit board for the playback unit. The track layout is given in the Appendix.

203

Operational amplifier A_1 is a non-inverting amplifier with variable amplification, to which a microphone output can be applied. This stage is also provided with a decoupling network (R_1-C_1) and an overvoltage network (R_4-D_1-D_2). Resistors R_{13} and R_{15} mix the microphone signal with the playback signal, and the resultant signal is applied to the output terminal via C_5. The output impedance of the unit is determined by R_{13} and R_{15}: with values as specified, it is about 1 kΩ.

Optional modifications

In some rare cases it may occur that the vocal signal is not at the centre of the sound, but is shifted slightly to the right or left. To ensure that even in those cases the vocal content is eradicated, the amplification of one of the channels must be altered. To do this accurately, replace R_{12} by a potentiometer (10 kΩ linear) in series with a 4.7 kΩ fixed resistor as shown in Figure 14-5.

Figure 14-5.
Circuit diagram of the
decoupling stage.

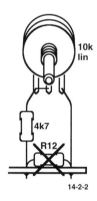

Components list

Resistors:
R_1–R_3 = 100 kΩ
R_4–R_6 = 470 Ω
R_7, R_{12}, R_{14} = 10 kΩ, 1%
R_8 = 22 kΩ
R_9 = 1 kΩ
R_{10}, R_{11} = 4.7 kΩ
R_{13} = 2.2 kΩ
R_{15} = 1.8 kΩ
P_1 = 47 kΩ, logarithmic

Capacitors:
$C_1 - C_3 = 0.33\,\mu F$
$C_4 = 0.22\,\mu F$
$C_5 = 1\,\mu F$ (not electrolotytic)

Semiconductors:
$D_1 - D_6$ = zener diode, 12 V, 500 mW

Integrated circuits:
$IC_1 = TL074$

Decoupling stage

The recording of large orchestras is often plagued by hum, which is caused by differing earth potentials. These result in small potential differences in the connecting
cables, which are clearly audible as hum on the music signal. This section describes
a circuit to remedy such problems. Since in most cases the hum disappears when
the signal earth is removed from the circuit earth, those in the present circuit are not
coupled directly but via high impedances. A differential amplifier removes the music
signal from the difference between the input signal and the signal on the associated earth lead.

Circuit description

The circuit diagram of the decoupling stage is shown in Figure 14-6. The upper part
of this diagram is well-known from previous circuits in this book. It is an impedance
converter with a decoupling network and overvoltage protection network. The input
earth is not directly linked to the circuit earth but via resistor R_3. The hum potential
which is normally dropped across the interconnecting wire is now dropped across
R_3. Diodes D_3 and D_4 limit the maximum permissible hum potential to ± 700 mV.
Normally, the hum voltage is much lower than this level.

    The second op amp operates as a differential amplifier, which produces a dif-
ferential voltage from the input signal and the signal on the earth line. This converts
the input signal referred to the signal line earth into a signal that is referred to the
circuit earth. The resulting signal is applied to the circuit output terminal via R_8 and
C_2.

Figure 14-6.
Circuit diagram of the
decoupling stage.

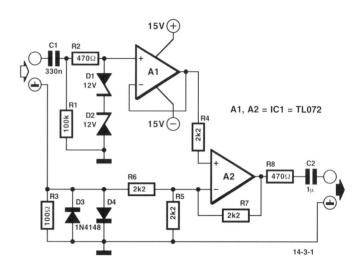

Figure 14-7.
Component layout of
the printed-circuit
board for the decou-
pling stage. The track
layout is given in the
Appendix.

Optional modifications

If the decoupling stage does not eliminate the hum, it may be necessary to increase the value of R_3 or leave it out altogether. If the hum is then still audible, it is in all likelihood caused by another phenomenon.

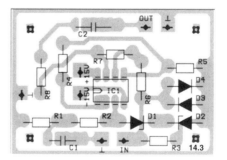

Component list

Resistors:
$R_1 = 100\ k\Omega$
$R_2, R_8 = 470\ \Omega$
$R_3 = 100\ \Omega$

R_4–R_7 = 2.2 kΩ, 1%

Capacitors:
C_1 = 0.33 μF
C_2 = 1 μF (not electrolytic)

Semiconductors:
D_1, D_2 = zener diode, 12 V, 500 mW
D_3, D_4 = 1N4148

Integrated circuits:
IC_1 = TL072

Pseudo-stereo circuit

The circuit described in this section converts a mono signal into a pseudo-stereo signal. It distorts the frequency response in such a way that several peaks and troughs ensue. The frequency responses of the two outputs of the circuit are each other's exact opposite so that the overall sound remains unchanged. If, for instance, at a given moment the frequency response of one output is a peak, that of the other is a trough—see Figure 14-8.

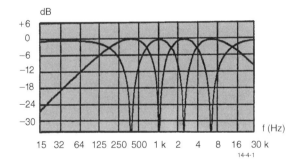

Figure 14-8.
The frequency responses at the two outputs of the circuit are each other's exact opposite.

Circuit description

In the circuit diagram of the pseudo-stereo unit in Figure 14-9, the five all-pass filters are represented by a box at the centre of the drawing.

The first stage, A_1 is an impedance converter that applies the input signal to the

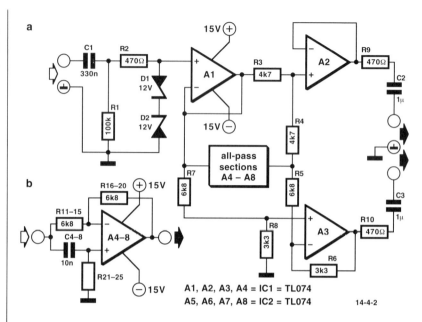

Figire 14-9.
Circuit diagram of the
pseudo-stereo unit.

A1, A2, A3, A4 = IC1 = TL074
A5, A6, A7, A8 = IC2 = TL074

14-4-2

all-pass filters and op amps A$_2$ and A$_3$.

Op amp A$_2$ mixes the output of A$_1$, that is, the original signal across R$_3$, with the phase-shifted signal from the all-pass filter across R$_4$. The frequency response of the resulting signal has several peaks and troughs. This action is exactly the same as that of the phaser in Chapter 11, except that here the peaks and troughs do not move about. The output of A$_2$ is applied to the upper circuit output terminals via R$_9$ and C$_2$.

The signal at the lower output is derived from op amp A$_3$ via C$_3$ and R$_{10}$. This op amp also mixes the original signal (across R$_7$) with a phase-shifted one (across R$_5$). Since A$_3$ is a differential amplifier, the signals are not added, however, but subtracted from one another. The resulting frequency response is exactly the opposite of that of the signal at the upper output terminals, so that the overall sound does not change. Either of the individual frequency ranges is then applied to the left-hand or right-hand channel as the case may be.

Figure 14-9b shows the circuit of one of the five all-pass filters. Apart from the values of resistors R$_{21}$–R$_{25}$, the filters are identical.

Components list

Resistors:

R$_1$ = 100 kΩ

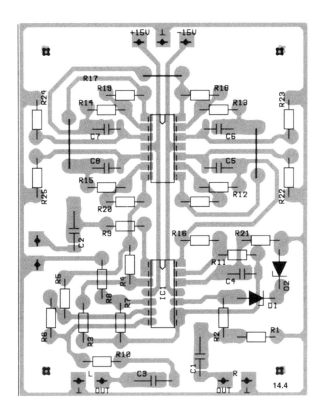

Figure 14-10.
Component layout of
the printed-circuit
board for the pseudo-
stereo unit. The track
layout is given in the
Appendix.

R_2, R_9, R_{10} = 470 Ω
R_3, R_4, R_{24} = 4.7 kΩ, 1%
R_5, R_7, R_{11}–R_{20} = 6.8 kΩ, 1%
R_6, R_8 = 3.3 kΩ, 1%
R_{21} = 33 kΩ $\approx$
R_{22} = 22 kΩ
R_{23} = 10 kΩ
R_{25} = 3.3 kΩ

Capacitors:
C_1 = 0.33 μF
C_2, C_3 = 1 μF (not electrolytic)
C_4–C_8 = 0.01 μF

Semiconductors:
D_1, D_2 = zener diode, 12 V, 500 mW
Integrated circuits:
IC_1, IC_2 = TL074

15. Ancillary circuits

The circuits described in this section are not designed for the actual processing of audio signals, but to aid the processing. The level indicator, for instance, enables audio equipment to be driven correctly. The noise generator enables straightforward control of the sound, while the sine wave generator produces a test signal that may prove useful in faultfinding.

Simple level indicator

When the drive level to an audio installation is low or insufficient, noise may become audible in the output. If, however, the drive level is too high, audible distortion results.

The circuit described in this section is useful for driving mixers and other audio equipment at the correct level. The drive level is monitored by two light-emitting diodes, LEDs. The green one lights when the level reaches 2 V_{pp}; when it flickersd, the drive level is correct. The red LED lights when the drive level exceeds 5 V_{pp}; it should not, or hardly ever, light.

The indicator circuit draws a current of 50 mA, indepent of the lighting of the LEDs.

Circuit description

The circuit diagram of the level indicator is shown in Figure 15-1. The circuit is built up from discrete components and uses three fairly uncommon inputs.

Resistor R_8, in conjunction with diode D_5, generates a voltage of at least –700 mV. Since the emitter of transistor T_2 is at this potential, its base voltage needs to be no higher than 0 V for the transistor to start conducting. This state is reached when the voltage at any of the three inputs exceeds 700 mV. When T_2 is one, there is no base voltage for T_4, so that this transistor cuts off. This results in a current through D_7 via resistor R_{10}, whereupon the diode lights. When the base voltage of T_2 drops below 0 V, or its emitter voltage below 700 mV, the transistor is cut off. Transistor T_4 is then switched on and short-circuits D_7 so that this diode does not light.

The red diode, D_6, is driven in a similar manner via T_1 and T_3. The requisite drive voltage for T_1 is, however, appreciably larger. This is essential, because on the one

Figure 15-1.
Circuit diagram of the
simple level indicator.

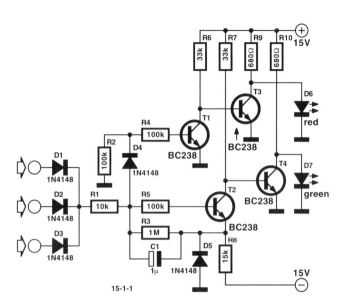

15-1-1

hand the threshold voltage (700 mV) of diode D_4 has to be overcome, and on the other, transistor T_1 needs a base bias of 700 mV (instead of 0 V as in the case of T_2) since its emitter is at earth potential.

Why three inputs?

Audio circuits normally have several stages that operate at different signal levels. In a preamplifier with tone control, for example, the signal level may be monitored before and after the tone control. That before the tone control may not cause the red LED on the indicator to light, although the tone control may well overdrive the preamplifier when the high frequencies or bass frequencies are heavily preemphasized. On the other hand, the preamplifier may well be overdriven, although the tone control masks this. A signal monitored after the tone control will, therefore,

Figure 15-2.
Here the three inputs
of the level indicator
are used to monitor
different points in an
audio circuit.

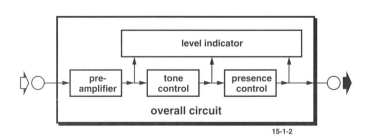

15-1-2

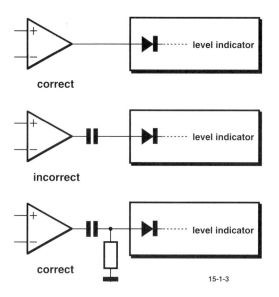

Figure 15-3.
Right and wrong ways
of linking signals to
the level indicator.

not result in the red LED lighting. This problem is overcome by monitoring the signals both before and after the tone control. The indicator circuit will automatically choose the largest of the three inputs and display this. Figure 15-2 shows a situation where all three inputs are used.

It is, of course, not necessary that all three inputs are used, but when they are used, they must be linked without any intervening decoupling network to the relevant signal source. If a capacitor is used for coupling, the indicator does not work correctly. If, however, for some reason there is no direct signal available and the relevant input of the indicator unit has to be linked to the signal source via a capaci-

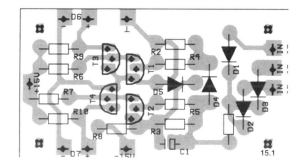

Figure 15-4.
Component layout of
the printed-circuit
board for the level in-
dicator. The track lay-
out is given in the
Appendix.

213

tor, the input should be connected to earth via a 10 kΩ resistor. See Figure 15-3.

Optional modifications

If required, the indicator may be fitted inside an audio equipment or provided with more than three inputs. Each additional input requires an additional diode. It is, of course, also possible to use only one input, in which case the superfluous two diodes may simply be omitted.

Components list

Resistors:
R_1 = 10 kΩ
R_2, R_4, R_5 = 100 kΩ
R_3 = 1 MΩ
R_6, R_7 = 33 kΩ
R_8 = 15 kΩ
R_9, R_{10} = 680 Ω

Capacitors:
C_1 = 1 μF, 16 v, radial

Semiconductors:
D_1–D_5 = 1N4148
D_6 = LED, red
D_7 = LED, green
T_1–T_4 = BC238

Drive level indicator

The level indicator described in this section enables a much more precise control of various signals than the one discussed in the previous section. A level range from −30 dB to +7 dB is covered by twelve light-emitting diodes, LEDs. The sensitivity, that is, the relationship between signal voltage and dB values, is set with a potentiometer.

Circuit description

The circuit diagram of the drive level indicator is divided into two: one, 15-5, the amplifier and rectifier section, and 15-6, the display circuit.

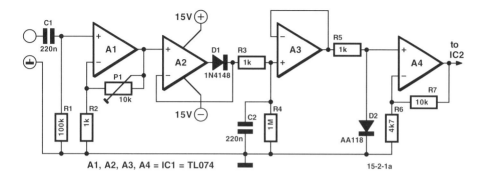

Figure 15-5.
Circuit diagram of the amplifier/rectifier section of the drive level indicator.

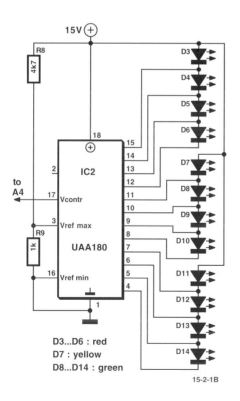

D3...D6 : red
D7 : yellow
D8...D14 : green

15-2-1B

Figure 15-6.
Circuit diagram of the display section of the drive level indicator.

215

The input signal is decoupled by R_1-C_1. Operational amplifier A_1 is a non-inverting amplifier whose amplification factor may be set between unity and $\times 10$.

Operational amplifier A_2, in conjunction with diode D_1, functions as a rectifier. When the signal at the non-inverting input of A_2 is positive, the op amp regulates its output so that the signals at its inputs are equal. Capacitor C_2 is discharged via R_3. When then the potential at the non-inverting input diminishes, which means that the voltage across the capacitor and that at the inverting input is higher, the op amp again regulates is output to equalize its two inputs. However, diode D_1 is then reverse biased so that the regulation action of the op amp is abortive. This means that capacitor C_2 can be charged by the op amp (via D_1) but not discharged, which can only take place via R_4. When the capacitor is being discharged, the drive level indicator is reset.

Operational amplifier A_3 functions as an impedance converter, which supplies the signal to potential divider R_5-D_2. Since germanium diodes have a non-linear resistance response, strong signals are attenuated to a greater degree than weak ones. The reason for selecting a germanium diode here is that IC_2 operates linearly, which for a display driver is not wholly satisfactory. The operating characteristic of D_2 converts the linear division of IC_2 in a virtually logarithmic display.

Operational amplifier A_4 raises the rectified signal by about $\times 3$ before it is applied to the display driver.

The display driver compares the input voltage at pin 17 with the preset reference voltages at pins 3 and 16. The potential at pin 16 sets the level at which the first LED should just not light. The voltage at pin 3 represents the level at which all the diodes should light.

Components list
Resistors:
$R_1 = 100\,k\Omega$
$R_2, R_3, R_5, R_9 = 1\,k\Omega$
$R_4 = 1\,M\Omega$
$R_6, R_8 = 4.7\,k\Omega$
$R_7 = 10\,k\Omega$
$P_1 =$ preset potentiometer, 10 kΩ, axial

Capacitors:
$C_1, C_2 = 0.22\,\mu F$

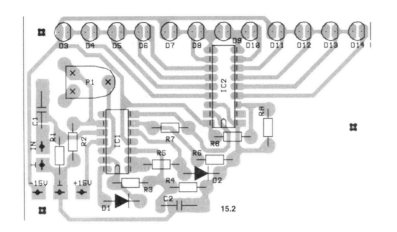

Figure 15-7.
Component layout of
the printed-circuit
board for the drive
level indicator. The
track layout is given in
the Appendix.

Semiconductors:
D_1 = 1N4148
D_2 = AA118 or similar
D_3–D_6 = LED, red
D_7 = LED, yellow
D_8–D_{14} = LED, green

Integrated circuits:
IC_1 = TL074
IC_2 = UAA180

diode	colour	level (dB)
D_3	red	+7
D_4	red	+6
D_5	red	+4
D_6	red	+2
D_7	yellow	0
D_8	green	−2
D_9	green	−5
D_{10}	green	−8
D_{11}	green	−12
D_{12}	green	−17
D_{13}	green	−23
D_{14}	green	−30

Table 15-1.
Correlating of the LED,
its colour and the sig-
nal level in dB.

Noise generator

Bascially, noise is a mixture of all audible frequencies, and this is why noise generators are often used for setting up equalizers. In combination with a spectrum analyser and a test microphone, a noise generator allows the frequency response of a loudspeaker and room acoustics to be measured accurately, and to arrive at the necessary compensation to be provided by an equalizer. But even without these instruments, a noise generator may be used to check a frequency response.

The circuit described in this section produces white noise, which may be converted into pink noise with a number of RC networks. A switch enables either type of noise to be selected. The signal level is set with a potentiometer.

Circuit description

In the circuit in Figure 15-8, the white noise is produced by transistor T_1, whose base-emitter junction draws current in the reverse bias direction via resistor R_2. The weak noise signal is applied to operational amplifier A_1 via capacitor C_1. The op amp amplifies the signal ×11 (determined by the ratio R_3:R_4).

The output of A_1 is applied to op amp A_2, which also amplifies the signal ×11 (here determined by the ratio R_5:R_6). Thus, at the output of A_2, the original noise signal has been amplified ×121. Network R_8-C_2 removes any residual direct voltage.

The decoupled output of A_2 is passed through a low-pass filter consisting of resistors R_9–R_{12} and capacitors C_4–C_6. The response of the filter has a slope of 3 dB per octave over the audio range, and converts the white noise into pink noise. Since the signal is attenuated by the filter, op amp A_3 provides an amplification of ×11.

Switch S_1 enables either the white noise output of A_2 or the pink noise output of A_3 to be selected.

Operational amplifier A_4 is an inverting amplifier whose amplification may be set between unity and ×4.7 with P_1. Its output is applied to the output terminals of the generator via R_{15} and C_7.

White noise is a random, undifferentiated signal having equal energy content at all frequencies; it sounds like the speech sibilant 'ss'.

Pink noise is a random, undifferentiated signal having equal energy within each octave of the audio spectrum. It sounds like the speech consonant 'ff'.

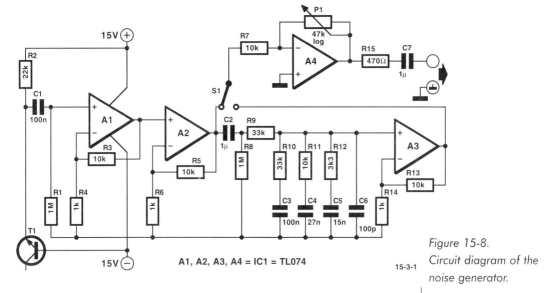

Figure 15-8.
Circuit diagram of the noise generator.

15-3-1

A1, A2, A3, A4 = IC1 = TL074

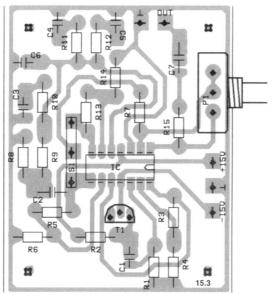

Figure 15-9.
Component layout of the printed-circuit board for the noise generator. The track layout is given in the Appendix.

Components list
Resistors:
R_1, R_8 = 1 MΩ

219

$R_2 = 22 \text{ k}\Omega$
$R_3, R_5, R_7, R_{11}, R_{13} = 10 \text{ k}\Omega$
$R_4, R_6, R_{14} = 1 \text{ k}\Omega$
$R_9, R_{10} = 33 \text{ k}\Omega$
$R_{12} = 3.3 \text{ k}\Omega$
$P_1 = 47 \text{ k}\Omega$, logarithmic

Capacitors:
$C_1, C_3 = 0.1 \text{ }\mu\text{F}, 5\%$
$C_2, C_7 = 1 \text{ }\mu\text{F}$ (not electrolytic)
$C_4 = 0.027 \text{ }\mu\text{F}, 5\%$
$C_5 = 0.015 \text{ }\mu\text{F}, 5\%$
$C_6 = 100 \text{ pF}, 5\%$

Semiconductors:
$T_1 = \text{BC238}$

Integrated circuits:
TL074

Sine wave test generator

The generator produces a sinusoidal signal at a very stable frequency of 1 kHz with very low distortion . The peak output may be set between 0 and 1 V r.m.s.

Circuit description

The circuit diagram of the sine wave generator is shown in Figure 15-10. The sine wave is generated by a Wien bridge circuit. Network R_1-R_2-C_1-C_2 is a band-pass filter whose resonant frequency is 1 kHz. The filter feeds back the output of A_1 to the input of the circuit. An amplification of at least ×3 is needed to ensure that the circuit oscillates, since the band-pass filter attenuates the oscillator signal by about ×3. The feedback causes a virtual earth at the inverting input of A_2, so that A_1 operates as a standard non-inverting amplifier. The amplification is determined by resistors R_3 and R_5 and amounts to $1 + R_5/R_3 = 3.2$, which meets the requirement for an amplification of ×3. Diodes D_1 and D_2 limit the amplifier output: as soon as the potential across R_5 exceeds a voltage range of ±600 mV, they are in parallel with the resistor and so reduce the amplification.

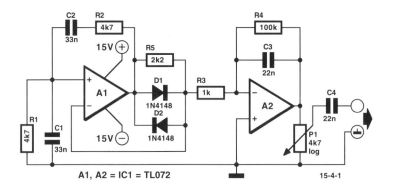

Figure 15-10.
Circuit diagram of
the sine wave test
generator.

Operational amplifier A_2 functions as an inverting integrator. Owing to capacitor C_3 in the feedback loop, the frequency response falls off at 6 dB/octave. This arrangement attenuates any harmonics so that the output of the op amp is a pure sine wave, which is applied to the generator output via C_4 and level control P_1.

Optional modifications
Since the frequency is determined by the equation

$$f = 1/2\pi RC,$$

it may be altered by changing the values of R_1, R_2, C_1, and C_2 as needed. In the equation, R represents both R_1 and R_2, and C, C_1 and C_2. Note that since the amplification of A_2 must remain the same, the value of C_3 also needs to be altered according to

$$C_3 = 1/45450f.$$

Components list
Resistors:
R_1, R_2 = 4.7 kΩ, 1%
R_3 = 1 kΩ, 1%
R_4 = 100 kΩ
R_5 = 2.2 kΩ, 1%
P_1 = 4.7 kΩ, logarithmic

Figure 15-11.
Component layout of
the printed-circuit
board for the sine
wave test generator.
The track layout is
given in the Appendix.

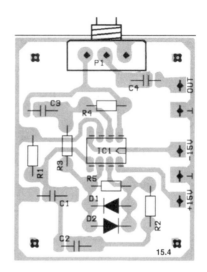

Capacitors:
$C_1, C_2 = 0.033\,\mu F$, 5%
$C_3 = 0.022\,\mu F$
$C_4 = 0.22\,\mu F$

Semiconductors:
$D_1, D_2 = 1N4148$

Integrated circuits:
$IC_1 = TL072$

16. Mixers

Mixers are needed in situations where several sound sources are to be blended. They range from a simple 2 or 3 into 1 combining unit without tone controls or level indication to sophisticated multi-channel into 4×4 matrix consoles.

When it is desired for each input channel to be provided with a preamplifier, tone control, and other refinements. Constructing a large mixer requires a good knowledge of audio electronics, dexterity and ... time. It is, however, undisputed that building one has advantages, other than cost, over a proprietary one. A home-made mixer can be given exactly the facilities desires, whereas a commercial one often has a number of unwanted facilities. Describing a design for such a complete construction would make little sense; it is far better to outline how the various single sections, such as preamplifier and tone control, are best combined in a mixer.

Block diagram

So as not to lose sight of the various facilities required from a mixer, it is best to start by drawing a diagram in which the basic sections of the mixer are represented by boxes as, for instance, in Figure 16-1. This is a block diagram of a simple 3-channel mixer.

The preamplifier circuits may be as shown in Figures 6-3 or 6-5, while the level indicator may be as described with Figure 15-1. The signal level in this is monitored before and after the tone control, so that any overloading shows up.

It is best to use logarithmic 10 kΩ slide potentiometers for the volume control.

The individual signals are best combined in an adder circuit as shown in Figure 16-2. In the case of large mixers, the number of inputs can be increased as needed. Each of these must be linked to the inverting input of the op amp via a 10 kΩ resistor as shown.

A mixer for stereo channels is rather more complex: the block diagram for a suitable 3-into-1 model is shown in Figure 16-3. In this setup, the input signals must be separated into a left-hand and right-hand component after they have passed through the preamplifier and tone control. The signal may be applied to the left-hand or right-hand adder, or to both, with the aid of a stereo balance control, which is normally included in the volume control section. The circuit diagram of such a

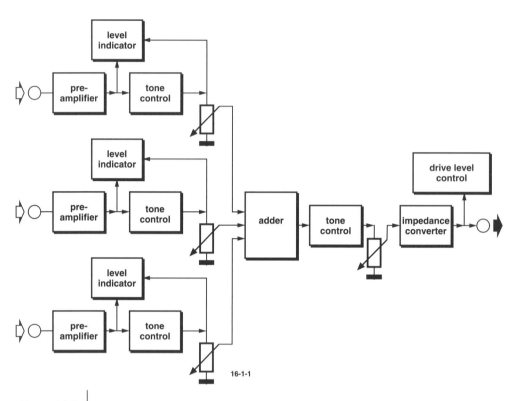

16-1-1

combined stereo balance control and volume is shown in Figure 16-4. In this, the signal at the wiper of the volume control is split into two components, one for the left-hand channel and one for the right-hand one, via 10 kΩ resistors. The stereo balance control earths a certain part, or the whole, of one of the signal components, so that the direction from which the relevant signal comes can be determined quite accurately.

inverting adder

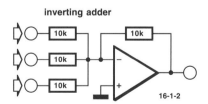

16-1-2

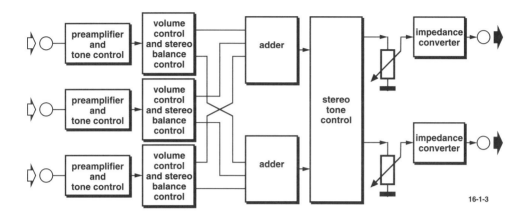

16-1-3

The two operational amplifiers serve two functions: they raise the level of the relevant signal ×2 to offset the attenuation of the balance control, and they ensure a low output impedance.

Figure 16-3. Block diagram of a 3-channel stereo mixer.

Figure 16-4. Circuit diagram of a combined stereo balance and volume control

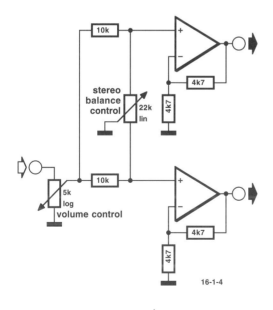

16-1-4

225

From single section to complete mixer

When the desired facilities have been incorporated in a block diagram, the circuit has to be decided. Several of the sections comprising the mixer may be constructed on the printed-circuit boards as described in earlier chapters of this book dealing with preamplifiers, tone controls and other circuit elements. It is, however, often more practical to design a complete circuit whose various elements for an input channel, containing a preamplifier, tone control and combined volume control and stereo balance control on a single board.

Depending on the application, the mixer may be given balanced or unbalanced inputs. If unbalanced inputs are used, it is advisable to provide each of them with a decoupling network as shown in Figure 14-6. This means that the input sockets must be isolated from the circuit earth, since that is then not the same as the input earth. If the mixer is to provide balanced outputs, each of these must be via an inverter as shown in Figure 16-5.

Figure 16-5. How to convert an unbalanced output into a balanced one with the aid of an inverter.

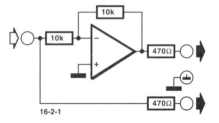

The enclosure of the mixer must be a metal one to which the circuit earth is bonded securely, which is the only way of ensuring that hum feedtrough is eliminated. The screen of the audio cables must also be bonded to the enclosure.

The power supply for mixers can be problematic since at any one time one or more input signals are amplified to a high degree. Any hum radiated by the mains transformer would be amplified to the same degree, so that the transformer should be as far away from the signal lines, particularly the input lines, as possible. It is, however, best to house the mains supply in a separate enclosure.

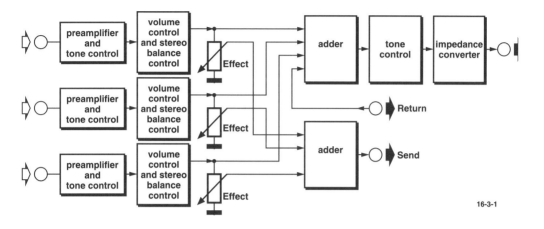

16-3-1

Effects and monitor paths

If it is desired to add effects to the various signals, it is, of course, necessary to provide relevant paths. These may be provides as shown in the block diagram in Figure 16-6. Each of the faders for the single signals and the master volume controls should be constructed as a potentiometer followed by an impedance converter to ensure that it outputs a low-impedance signal. This combination is followed by a potentiometer for controlling the path of the relevant effect. Like the main signals, the effects signals are combined in two adder. The output of one of these is applied to the relevant effects units(s) via the send terminal. The output of the effects unit(s) is returned via the return terminal an applied to the other adder, from where it is applied to the master volume control via yet another tone control. Stereo mixers need two return terminals, one for the left-hand and the other for the right-hand channel. This enables stereo effects units to be used.

In principle, the effects paths may be used as monitor path: the send terminal is then the monitor output, while the return terminal is not used. It should be noted that the setting of the relevant fader(s) affects the output of the monitor. If this is not acceptable, the signal for the relevant monitor must be taken directly from the preamplifier. In many mixers, the monitor signals may be taken from either via a change-over switch.

Figure 16-6. Diagram showing paths for adding effects to the various single signals.

227

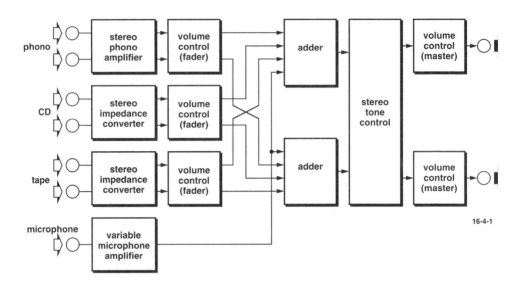

Figure 16-7.
Block diagram of a
disco mixer.

Disco mixer

A disco mixer is invariably provided with stereo inputs as shown in Figure 16-7. The tape and CD inputs do not need a preamplifier, since the relevant units provide a high enough output. The phono input, however, needs a special phono preamplifier. The microphone input should have a variable preamplifier such as the general purpose preamplifier described in Chapter 6. The volume controls must, of course, be stereo potentiometers.

Appendix: Track layouts

Most of the track layouts given in the Appendix are on a scale 1:1; when this is not so, the relevant scale is stated.

Contents:

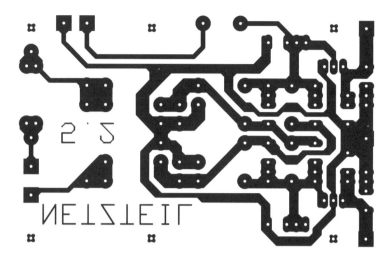

Figure 5-3.

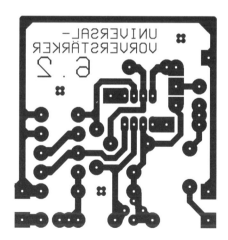

Figure 6-4.

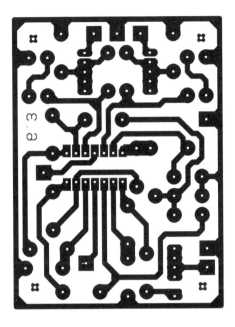

Figure 6-6.

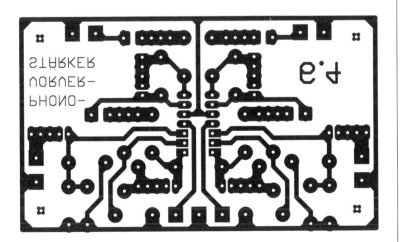

Figure 6-9.

233

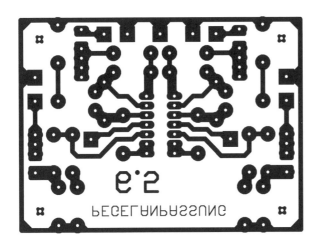

Figure 6-11.

Figure 8-3.

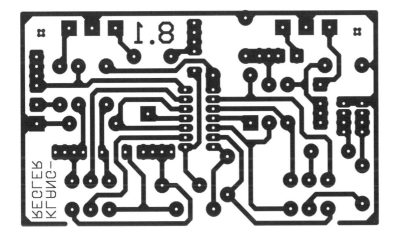

235

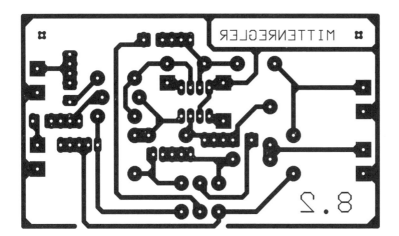

Figure 8-6.

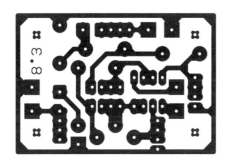

Figure 8-10.

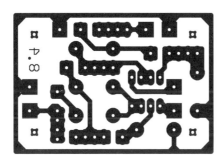

Figure 8-13.

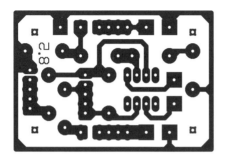

Figure 8-16.

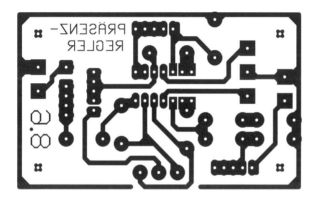

Figure 8-18.

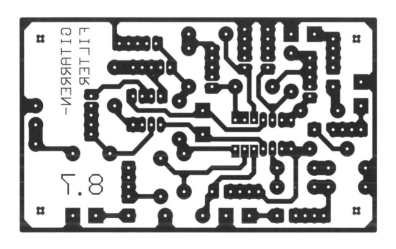

Figure 8-21.

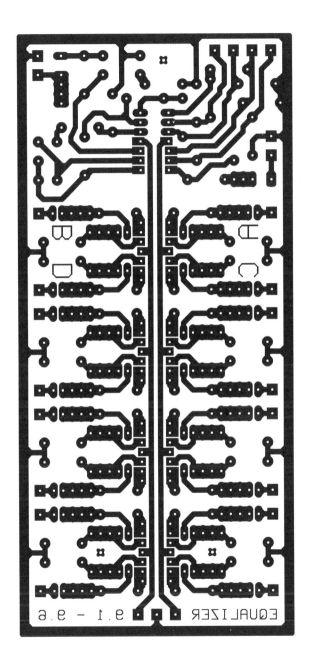

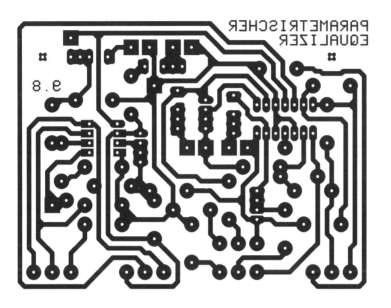

PARAMETRISCHER
EQUALIZER

9.8

Figure 9-17.

243

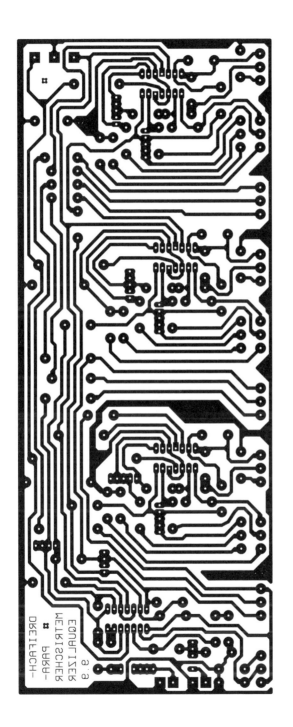

Figure 9-20
70% of true size

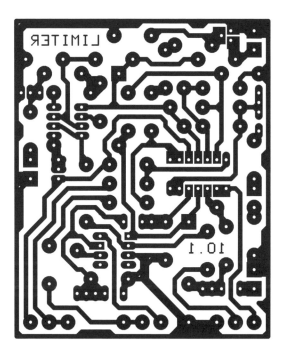

Figure 10-2

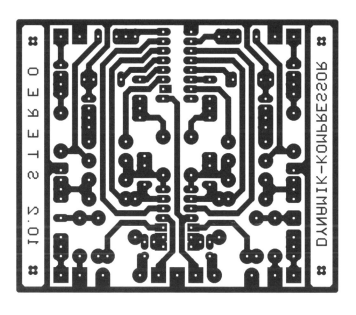

Figure 10-5

247

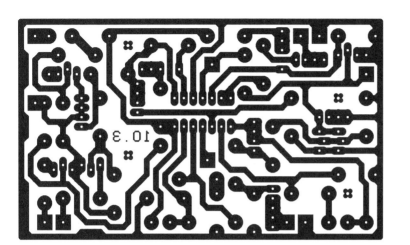

Figure 10-7

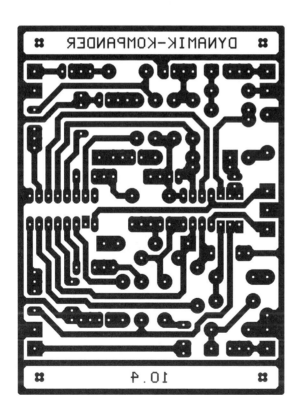

Figure 10-11

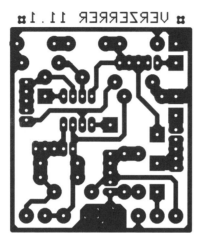

Figure 11-2

Figure 11-4

Figure 11-8

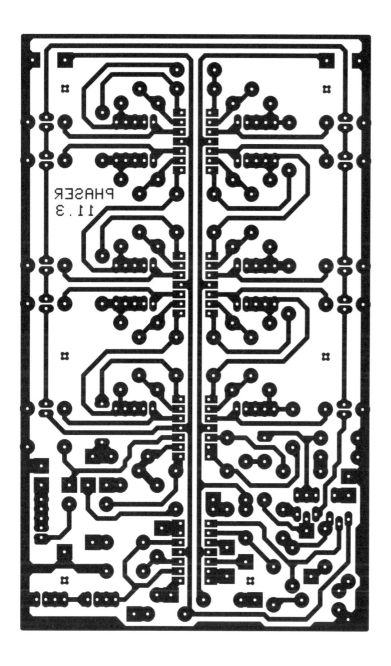

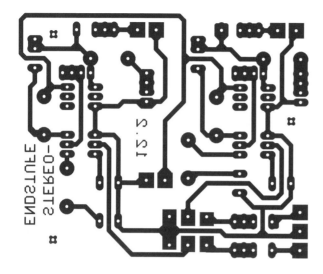

Figure 12-8

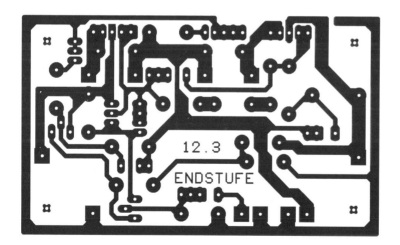

Figure 12-12

255

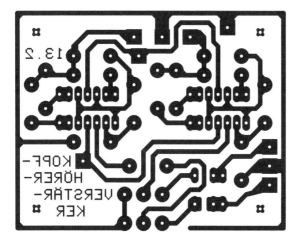

Figure 13-3

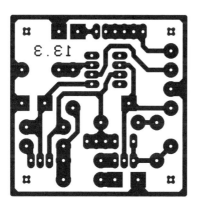

Figure 13-5

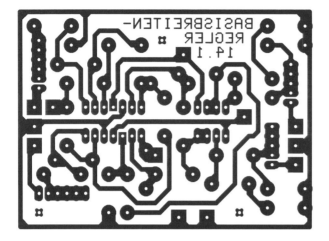

Figure 14-2

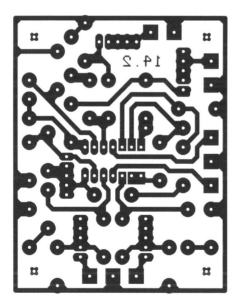

Figure 14-4

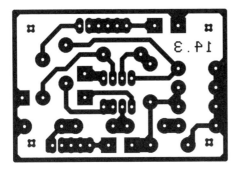

Figure 14-7

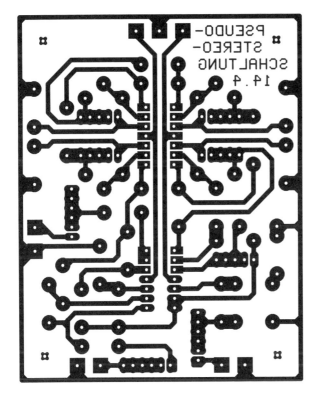

Figure 14-10

Figure 15-4

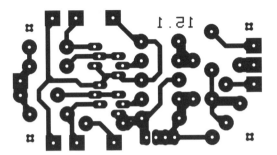

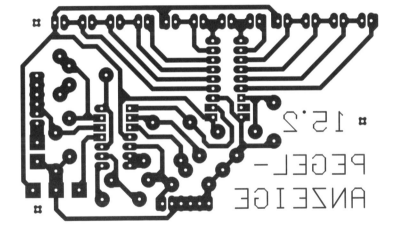
Figure 15-7

263

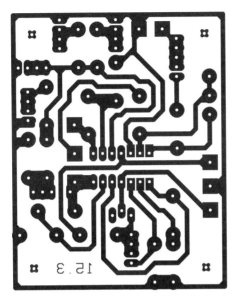

Figure 15-9

Figure 15-11

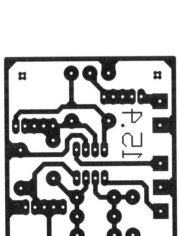

Index